Spelling: WORDS and SKILLS

Authors

Ronald L. Cramer
W. Dorsey Hammond
Lida F. Lim
John Prejza, Jr.
DeWayne Triplett

Reader Consultants

R. Scott Bradshaw
Alberta J. London

Scott, Foresman and Company
Editorial Offices: Glenview, Illinois

Regional Sales Offices: Palo Alto, California •
Tucker, Georgia • Glenview, Illinois •
Oakland, New Jersey • Dallas, Texas

Here are some steps to help you study your words.

Before you write each word:
    Look at the word.
    Look at the letters.
    Say the word.
    Listen to the sounds.
When you write each word:
    Copy the word from your list.
    Write the word without looking at it.
After you write each word:
    Check the word with your list.
    Did you make a mistake?
    Notice where you made the mistake and
        begin the steps again.

Each regular lesson in this book has four parts:
Part A gives the word list.
Part B is a practice page.
Part C includes proofreading, dictionary, and handwriting work.
Part D has extra lists of words you can learn.

Every sixth lesson is a review lesson. After taking a test at the end of each regular lesson, record your misspelled or most troublesome words under the heading **Personal Words** in the review lesson.

You will see symbols like /a/ in lessons in this book. These symbols stand for sounds. For example, /a/ stands for the sound of the letter **a** in *cat*.

ISBN 0-673-12736-2

Copyright © 1981, 1978
Scott, Foresman and Company, Glenview, Illinois.
All Rights Reserved.
Printed in the United States of America.

2 3 4 5 6 7 8 9 10 11 12 –RRC– 88 87 86 85 84 83 82 81

CONTENTS

THE VOWEL SOUNDS /a/, /e/, /i/, /o/, AND /u/

Part A

Say the words in the list below. Write the words.

1. than
2. shall
3. passed
4. camera
5. well
6. bench
7. plenty
8. elementary
9. milk
10. pink
11. crystal
12. physics
13. mysterious
14. block
15. monsters
16. comedy
17. funds
18. crutches
19. minutes *
20. interrupt *

The sounds /a/, /e/, /i/, /o/, and /u/ are usually spelled with a single vowel letter, as **a** in *than*. Circle the letters that spell the short vowel sounds in the list words.

● Write the first list word for each vowel spelling.

/a/   /e/   /i/   /o/   /u/

∗Wild Words   We all know that an hour is broken down into units called *minutes*. But did you know that the record of what is said in a meeting is called *the minutes?*

Don't interrupt good spelling by forgetting the double **r** in *interrupt.*

Part B

1. Write the words that fit each clue.

   /a/ spelled **a**   /i/ spelled **y**   /o/ spelled **o**

2. Select a word from the list for each definition.

   a. a long seat
   c. blend of red and white
   e. walking aids
   g. before high school

   b. a white liquid
   d. enough
   f. sums of money
   h. hole for oil or water

3. Write the list words that fit the story below.

   Late last night, I was eating cookies and drinking (a) .
   I was also watching a very funny (b) show on TV. Then a
   woman came on the screen and said, "We (c) this
   program to bring you this message. A man has reported
   seeing a (d) spacecraft. Two strange (e) came out of the
   ship. The man took their picture with his (f) ."
   Was I scared! But I've never been happier (g) when I
   woke up and knew it was just a dream.

What's the Big Idea?

The short vowel sounds /a/, /e/, /i/, /o/, and /u/ are
usually spelled **a, e, i** or **y, o,** and **u.**

Dictionary

Many words have more than one meaning. Look at this dictionary entry for the word *bench.*

bench (bench), **1** a long seat, with or without a back, usually of wood or stone. **2** court of law. **3** take (a player) out of a game.

Notice that the meanings are numbered. Use *bench* in three sentences, one for each meaning.

One dictionary lists 47 definitions for *run.* How many uses can you think of? Here are some examples.

a run of luck, a mill run
run a red light, water runs

Now try the words *set* and *hit.*

set	*hit*
set the table	hit the ball
a hen sets	hit song
set of dishes	hit the road

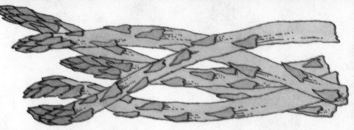

Part D

Choose the list or lists of words you want to learn. Then complete the activities next to each list you choose.

---

1. Write the word that means the opposite of:
   a. then   b. yes

2. Write the word that means about the same as:
   a. have been   b. desiring

Review Words

were

wanting

no

now

---

1. What two words might you hear in a hospital?

2. Write the word that can mean the same as:
   a. stress   b. exercise

Big Idea Words

emphasis

activity

operate

examine

Write a challenge word for each clue.

1. food cooked and served in the same dish

2. two vegetables

3. a white fatty substance found in the body

Challenge Words

casserole

cholesterol

asparagus

cauliflower

Study Hint!

Look at each word and pronounce it. Then write the word without looking at it. Check the spelling. Write each word correctly two times.

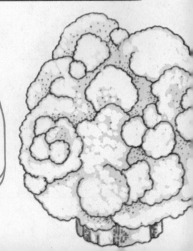

LESSON 2
THE VOWEL SOUNDS
/ā/, /ē/, /ī/, and /ō/

Part A

Say the words in the list below. Write the words.

1. angel
2. bacon
3. basic
4. patriot
5. senior
6. equal
7. ingredient
8. museum
9. diet
10. private

11. trial
12. hotel
13. solar
14. control
15. dynamite
16. python
17. hyphen
18. cycle
19. obey *
20. bologna *

● Write the first list word for each spelling pattern below.
/ā/ spelled **a**   /ē/ spelled **e**   /ī/ spelled **i**
/ī/ spelled **y**   /ō/ spelled **o**
● Write the first list word in which the given vowel sound is in the second syllable.   /ē/   /ō/
● Circle the letters that spell /ā/, /ē/, /ī/, and /ō/.

*Wild Words   In *obey,* the letters **ey** are an unusual spelling for /ā/.

Remember that *bologna* ends with the letter **a** regardless of which way you pronounce it.

Test Score: _____ —20   **8**   Part A Score: _____ —30

Part B

1. Write the words that begin with these long vowel sounds.
   /ō/   /ā/   /ē/

2. Write the words that contain /ē/.

3. Three words have /ā/ at the end of the first syllable. Write these words.

4. Write the four words that have /ī/ spelled **y**.

5. Write the words that rhyme with the following:
   a. dial   b. motel

6. Write the word that goes with each clue.
   a. having to do with the sun
   b. to follow rules
   c. power or authority
   d. large sausage
   e. to restrict food
   f. the opposite of *public*

Underline the letters that stand for the long vowel sounds in the words above.

What's the Big Idea?

In words of two or more syllables, long vowel sounds are often spelled with one vowel letter.

Proofreading

The following notice might have been posted in colonial times. Find three words that should start with capitals and four misspelled words and write them correctly.

Paytriots'! Support the american colonies! help us achieve eqiull justice for all privit citizens. until there is basec justice for everyone, there will be no justice for anyone.

Handwriting

overhill stroke / loop   Practice the overhill stroke and the loop below the line in the letter **y** as you write *dynamite* and *python*.

SPELLBOUND

Use list words to complete the crossword puzzle.

ACROSS
1. limit food
3. where art objects are displayed
5. fundamental
7. loyal citizen
8. strips of pork
9. court procedure

DOWN
2. the same as
4. the older or graduating class
6. huge sausage
7. a kind of snake

Part D

Choose the list or lists of words you want to learn. Then complete the activities next to each list you choose.

Write the review words that were left out of the sentences.

(1) fun to watch my kitten. Yesterday it (2) around in circles chasing (3) tail but couldn't catch (4) .

Review Words

it
it's
its
went

---

1. Say each word. Write the word that has the given vowel sound in the second syllable.

   /ā/   /ī/   /ē/   /ō/

2. Write two list words in which you hear /ā/, /ē/, /ī/, or /ō/ in the first syllable.

Big Idea Words

suppose
engrave
confide
immediate

---

1. Unscramble the letters and write each word correctly.

   a. a small flute
      (lpoicco)

   b. like a trumpet
      (torcen)

   c. a brass instrument
      with sliding tube
      (brotnemo)

   d. a woodwind instrument
      (ooeb)

2. Write the words that contain /ō/ in the final syllable.

Content Words

oboe
piccolo
trombone
cornet

Study Hint!

Look at a word and pronounce it. Cover the word, write it, and then check the spelling. When you feel sure that you can spell the word correctly, study the next word.

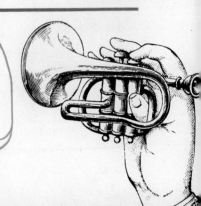

11

MORE SPELLINGS FOR /ā/, /ē/, and /ō/

Part A

Say the words in the list below. Write the words.

1. coal
2. toad
3. approach
4. fellow
5. following
6. hollow
7. gain
8. acquainted
9. complain
10. spray
11. delay
12. driveway
13. steep
14. needle
15. freedom
16. cream
17. meanwhile
18. underneath
19. nowhere *
20. though *

The list words contain the sounds /ā/ as in *cake*, /ē/ as in *eve*, and /ō/ as in *nose*.

● In what two ways is /ō/ spelled in words 1–6?
/ā/ spelled in words 7–12? /ē/ spelled in words 13–18?
/ō/ spelled in the wild words?

✲Wild Words *Nowhere* is a compound word. Remember that it is made of *no + where*. It is NOT *now + here*.

Though means "although" or "in spite of the fact that."
Though it rhymes with *no*, /ō/ is spelled **o-u-g-h.**

Part B

1. Read the paragraph below and underline list words.

   José and Maria were following a puppy. They'd seen the little fellow shoved from a car that sped away. He was cream colored with spots like coal around his eyes. When the children had tried to approach the puppy to become acquainted with him, the frightened animal had crawled into a hollow pipe underneath a steep driveway. José ran to the other end of the pipe without delay. Meanwhile Maria started to crawl in after the puppy. The animal could not gain freedom. Perhaps Grandma would let the children keep the unwanted puppy.

2. Copy from the paragraph list words that contain the sounds given below.

   /ō/ as in *nose*   /ē/ as in *eve*   /ā/ as in *cake*

3. Write a list word that rhymes with each word below.

   explain   elsewhere   so

4. Write the list word that goes with each picture.

a.

b.

c.

What's the Big Idea?

The sound /ā/ is often spelled **ai** or **ay**; /ō/ is often spelled **oa** or **ow**; and /ē/ is often spelled **ee** or **ea**.

Dictionary

Look up in the glossary each underlined word in the sentences below. Write the number of the glossary definition that fits the meaning of the underlined word.

1. A small village was nestled in the <u>hollow</u>.
2. The campers used a <u>hollow</u> gourd as a cup.
3. Al thought his <u>fellow</u> classmates disliked him.
4. "Quiet, <u>fellow</u>!" Mr. Lee commanded the puppy.
5. Joan brushed a pine <u>needle</u> from her jacket.
6. Grandpa discovered that the baby had his lost knitting <u>needle</u>.
7. "How do you <u>cream</u> butter, Mom?" Geno asked as he read the cookie recipe.
8. Carla chose the <u>cream</u> of her rock collection for the exhibit.

Handwriting

fr   ch

Notice how the letter **r** is joined to the bottom loop of the letter **f** and how the uphill stroke of the **c** forms part of the **h**. Practice joining **fr** and **ch** as you write *freedom* and *approach*.

SPELLBOUND

Have you ever discovered errors in signs in shop windows or along streets and highways? Look at this photograph of a sign. Find the misspelled word and write it correctly. Start a collection of errors you and your classmates notice in signs and other printed materials.

Choose the list or lists of words you want to learn. Then complete the activities next to each list you choose.

Review Words

1. Which word is always capitalized?
2. Write the past tense of *happen.*
3. Write the review word that rhymes with each word below.
   a. fanned   b. day
4. Use the review words in a story about something interesting that happened to you and some friends.

happened
I
and
they

Challenge Words

1. Write a challenge word for each definition.
   a. a colorful print   b. a fine, soft wool
   c. made by human skill   d. any woven material
2. Use the challenge words in a news article about back-to-school clothing styles.

a. paisley
b. cashmere
c. synthetic
d. textile

Content Words

Write the content word that rhymes with each word below.
1. conversation   2. narrow
3. vulture   4. advertise

harrow
cultivation
fertilize
agriculture

Study Hint!

When you have difficulty spelling a word, check carefully to see which part is giving you trouble. When a part of a word is not spelled the way it sounds, you will have to memorize the spelling of the word.

CONSONANT SOUNDS

Part A

Say the words in the list below. Write the words.

1. schoolmate
2. schedule
3. scholarship
4. splash
5. split
6. splinter
7. screaming
8. scrooge
9. scrape
10. screen
11. unless
12. embarrass
13. missile
14. different
15. office
16. cliff
17. accused
18. soccer
19. business *
20. necessary *

- In words 1–3, /sk/ is spelled ____.
- In words 4–6, /spl/ is spelled ____.
- In words 7–10, /skr/ is spelled ____.
- In words numbered ____ to ____, double consonants stand for one sound.
- Circle the double consonants in the list words.

*Wild Words   In *business,* the first **s** stands for /z/ and the double **s** at the end stands for /s/.

In *necessary,* **c** stands for the first /s/ and the double **s** stands for the second /s/.

Part B

1. Write three words that begin with the sounds /sk/.

2. Write four words that begin with /skr/.

3. Write three words that begin with /spl/.

4. Write four words that end with a double consonant.

5. Write two words in which the letter **c** is doubled.

6. Write the word that goes with each clue below.
   a. rocket
   b. required
   c. not the same
   d. place for business

7. Write the word that rhymes with each word given.
   a. winter
   b. green
   c. trash
   d. tape

8. A few English words come from characters in books. In *A Christmas Carol,* by Charles Dickens, there is a greedy, stingy character named Ebenezer Scrooge. Which list word is sometimes used to describe a greedy, stingy person?

What's the Big Idea?

The blends /sk/ spelled **sch**, /skr/ spelled **scr**, and /spl/ spelled **spl** appear at the beginning of words and syllables. The double consonants **rr, ss, ff,** and **cc** are often used to spell a single consonant sound.

Proofreading

Ron had a friend called Bobo who was always noticing humorous double meanings in the use of words. Ron wrote down some of Bobo's jokes, but he forgot two sets of quotation marks and two capital letters in direct quotes. Write the words that begin and end the quotes that are incorrect. Add the quotation marks and capitals. Write the five misspelled words correctly.

Bobo asked, "If an athlete gets athlete's foot, what does an astronaut get?"

"I don't know. What?" asked Ron.

"Missle toe," laughed Bobo.

Bill said, here comes Ann with the ball. Now we can play soker.

Bobo replied, "I like Ann. I don't want to hit her."

my older sister is going to the University of Paris on a scolarship, said Sue.

"Why doesn't she go on a jet?" asked Bobo. "All the deffrent ships are so slow for neccesary travel.

SPELLBOUND

Begin with each word given below and change or add one letter at a time to make words that match the clues given. The last words will be list words.

1.   it
2. — — — lighted
3. — — — — a straight cut or tear
4. — — — — — to break or cut from end to end

5.   team
6. — — — — a very large quantity
7. — — — — — part of milk
8. — — — — — — a loud, sharp cry

Choose the list or lists of words you want to learn. Then complete the activities next to each list you choose.

---

1. Write the words that have double consonants.
2. Write the word in which three letters represent /sk/.

Big Idea Words

assemble
differ
occur
school

Write the name of each flower and then unscramble the letters to check your answer.

1. unteipa   2. tihaycnh   3. ddifolfa   4. ilodarmg

Challenge Words

daffodil
marigold
hyacinth
petunia

- A collection of stories or poems is an *anthology*.
- Writings of the highest quality are called *classics*.
- A changing from one language into another is a *translation*.
- One who judges writing, art, or music is a *critic*.

Write the words that correctly complete the sentence.

One __(1)__ said that the __(2)__ contains many __(3)__ , including one selection that is a __(4)__ from Russian.

Content Words

classics
anthology
translation
critic

Study Hint!

Make your own spelling dictionary. Use a page for each letter of the alphabet. List those words you have had trouble spelling before. Review your words regularly.

THE CONSONANT SOUNDS /s/ and /z/

Part A

Say the words in the list below. Write the words.

1. same
2. sandwich
3. oasis
4. purpose
5. promise
6. century
7. icicle
8. once
9. practice
10. resort

11. using
12. prison
13. thousand
14. blaze
15. bulldozer
16. frozen
17. horizon
18. quiz
19. bazaar *
20. dessert *

The sound /s/ is commonly spelled **s**, or **se**, and **c**, or **ce**.

● Write the first list word for each spelling.

The sound /z/ is commonly spelled **s** or **z**.

● Write the first list word for each spelling.

✱Wild Words   Note that the second vowel sound in the word *bazaar* is spelled **aa**.

The word *dessert* is often confused with the noun *desert*. Notice that **ss** in *dessert* stands for /z/.

Part B

1. Write the words from 1–18 in which /s/ is spelled:

   s, s, s;   se, se;   c, c;   ce, ce

2. Write the words from 1–18 in which /z/ is spelled:

   s, s, s, s;   z, z, z, z, z

3. In which wild word does **ss** stand for /z/?

4. Which wild word has the second vowel sound spelled **aa**?

5. Write a list word to complete each sentence below.

   a. A ＿＿ is an area full of small shops where you can buy different things.

   b. I bought some honey cakes there for ＿＿.

   c. My sister made me ＿＿ to buy her some beads to make a necklace.

   d. It was hard to find enough beads that were all the ＿＿ so I bought her some different kinds.

   e. It was exciting to be there, and I would really like to go back at least ＿＿ more.

What's the Big Idea?

The sound /s/ may be spelled **s**, or **se**, and **c**, or **ce**.
The sound /z/ is commonly spelled **s** or **z**.

Dictionary

Some entries in dictionaries have diagrams. Often the diagrams have captions and labels that help you learn more about the entry. Look at the example below and then answer the questions.

diagram with labels

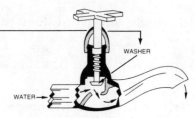

entry

fau cet (fô′sit), device containing a valve for turning on or off a flow of liquid from a pipe or a container holding it; tap; spigot. *n.*

faucet—partly cut away to show water flow when the handle is turned to raise the disk-shaped washer. When the washer is screwed down over the circular opening the water flow stops. .

caption

1. Which tells you that a faucet can also be called a "tap," the caption or the entry?
2. Which shows you the direction water can flow through a faucet, the diagram or the entry?
3. Which tells you how to stop the flow of water in a faucet, the caption or the entry?

 # SPELLBOUND

Many words come from people's names. Match the names on the left with the words on the right. Use your glossary to find out more about the words.

1. Earl of Sandwich   a. Ferris wheel
2. Amelia J. Bloomer   b. curium
3. Countess Cinchón   c. sandwich
4. Marie and Pierre Curie d. cinchona
5. George Ferris   e. bloomers

Part D

Choose the list or lists of words you want to learn. Then complete the activities next to each list you choose.

Write the review word that fits each clue.
1. an adult female person
2. plural for *child*
3. your aunt's child
4. an officer

Review Words

cousin

woman

children

captain

---

1. Write the words that complete the sentences.

Warning: _(a)_ smoking is _(b)_ to your health.
To please is to _(c)_ .
Trans- means "across" and *fuse* comes from a Latin word which means "to pour." To change blood from one person to another is to _(d)_ blood.

2. Write the list words that end in /s/ spelled **s**, **se**, or **ce**.

Big Idea Words

satisfy

cigarette

transfuse

hazardous

Use the numbers to match the words with the sentences.

This room is too dark. We need to _(2)_ it more.
These _(3)_ window shades keep the light out.
A _(1)_ separates light into many colors.
A rainbow has all the colors of the _(4)_ .

Challenge Words

1. prism
2. illuminate
3. opaque
4. spectrum

Study Hint!

Divide your list words into groups: /s/ spelled **c**, /s/ spelled **s**, /z/ spelled **s**, and /z/ spelled **z**. Study each group together.

REVIEW

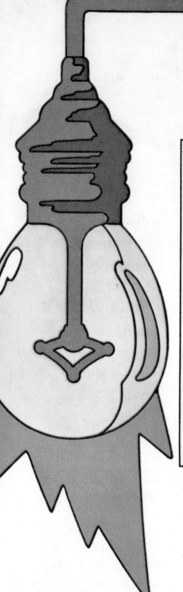

Here are some steps to help you study your words.

Before you write each word:
    Look at the word.
    Look at the letters.
    Say the word.
    Listen to the sounds.
When you write each word:
    Copy the word from your list.
    Write the word without looking at it.
After you write each word:
    Check the word with your list.
    Did you make a mistake?
    Notice where you made the mistake and begin
      the steps again.

Write the five review words for each lesson. Did you remember to record your misspelled or most troublesome words after the lesson test? If you forgot, write any you think of now under the heading Personal Words.

Lesson 1: The Vowel Sounds /a/, /e/, /i/, /o/, and /u/

Review Words	Personal Words
1. than	1. _____
2. funds	2. _____
3. crutches	3. _____
4. minutes✳	4. _____
5. interrupt✳	5. _____

Lesson 2: The Vowel Sounds /ā/, /ē/, /ī/, and /ō/

Review Words	Personal Words
1. patriot	1. _____
2. control	2. _____
3. dynamite	3. _____
4. obey*	4. _____
5. bologna*	5. _____

Lesson 3: More Spellings for /ā/, /ē/, and /ō/

Review Words	Personal Words
1. acquainted	1. _____
2. needle	2. _____
3. meanwhile	3. _____
4. nowhere*	4. _____
5. though*	5. _____

Lesson 4: Consonant Sounds

Review Words	Personal Words
1. schedule	1. _____
2. different	2. _____
3. office	3. _____
4. business*	4. _____
5. necessary*	5. _____

Lesson 5: The Consonant Sounds /s/ and /z/

Review Words	Personal Words
1. sandwich	1. _____
2. once	2. _____
3. practice	3. _____
4. bazaar*	4. _____
5. dessert*	5. _____

1. Write words that have the following spellings. The letters show how many review words to write. The *L* inside parentheses stands for *Lesson*.

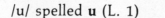

/u/ spelled **u** (L. 1)   /i/ spelled **i** (L. 1)

a. _____   a. _____

b. _____   b. _____

c. _____

/ō/ spelled **o** (L. 2)   /s/ spelled **c** (L. 4,5)

a. _____   a. _____

b. _____   b. _____

c. _____   c. _____

d. _____

2. Write five review words that contain a double consonant. (L/ 4.5)

3. Write two compound words. (L. 3)

4. Use the pronunciation clues to write review words to complete the phrases below.

  a. bigger *(ŦHan)* you
  b. a classroom *(skej′ ůl)*
  c. an American *(pā′ trē ə t)*
  d. a stick of *(dī′ nə mīt)*
  e. *(ə kwān′ tid)* with him
  f. *(nē′ dl)* in a haystack
  g. even *(ŦHō)* it's raining
  h. a fried-egg *(sand′ wich)*
  i. *(wuns)* upon a time
  j. a school *(bə zär′)*

5. Write the review word that means the same as or reminds you of the words below.

Clue	Review Word
a. a meat sausage	_____
b. just one time	_____
c. money	_____
d. TNT	_____
e. Hero, Hoagy, sub	_____
f. ice cream and cake	_____
g. 1 hour = 60	_____
h. Paul Revere	_____
i. supports to help a person walk	_____

Test Yourself

Find the correct spelling for each word.
1. bisness, business, buisness
2. practice, pratice, practise
3. thogh, though, thow
4. obay, obae, obey
5. balogna, balona, bologna
6. interrup, interrupt, interupt
7. cruches, cruthes, crutches
8. necesary, necessary, neccessary

Personal Words

Make a list of clues like the one at the top of the page for as many of your personal words as possible.

Write your personal words in three lists: (1) words that contain a long vowel sound, (2) words that contain a double letter, (3) other words.

MORE SPELLINGS FOR
/ā/, /ī/, /ō/, and /ē/

Part A

Say the words in the list below. Write the words.

1. brave
2. pace
3. became
4. twice
5. wise
6. advice
7. meteorite
8. type
9. style
10. paralyze
11. analyze
12. pole
13. postpone
14. telescope
15. envelope
16. gasoline
17. automobile
18. magazine
19. furnace *
20. skis *

In the word *brave* the vowel letter **a** is followed by a consonant letter and a final **e**. The vowel sound /ā/ is spelled **a-e**. Circle the letters that spell the sound.

● Tell how each vowel sound is spelled in these words.

/ā/ pace	/ī/ twice	/ī/ type
/ō/ pole	/ē/ gasoline	

*Wild Words   Since the last syllable of *furnace* is unaccented, you do not say /ā/ as in *pace.*

Do not confuse *skis* with *skies,* the plural of *sky.*

Part B

1. Write the list words that follow each pattern.

   a. /ī/ spelled **i-e**
   b. /ī/ spelled **y-e**
   c. /ō/ spelled **o-e**
   d. /ā/ spelled **a-e**
   e. /ē/ spelled **i-e**

2. Write the list words that complete the sentences.

   The old house has a coal-burning (a) .
   The girls were eager to try their new (b) on the ski slopes.
   The astronomer was watching the skies through a (c) when he saw a (d) fall to the earth.
   He bought a (e) that contains two articles which (f) the problem of pollution.
   The doctor decided to (g) the operation until he could tell whether the injury would (h) the boy.

GASOLINE

What's the Big Idea?

Vowel sounds such as /ā/, /ē/, /ī/, and /ō/ are often spelled with a vowel letter and a final **e** separated by a consonant letter.

Dictionary

In English words of two or more syllables, one syllable is stressed, or accented, more than the others. Some words have two accented syllables. A primary accent is stronger than a secondary accent.

Say each word given in pronunciation symbols. Place the primary (ˊ) and secondary (ˊ) accent marks where you think they should be. Then check the words in the glossary. Notice that two words are listed twice.

(ô tə mə bēl)   (mag ə zēn)   (mag ə zēn)   (gas ə lēn)
(gas ə lēn)

Are your pronunciations shown in the glossary?

SPELLBOUND

Use list words to complete the crossword puzzle.

ACROSS

1. two times
3. a manner of doing things
6. rate of movement
8. a meteor that reaches earth
11. instrument used by astronomers
12. to examine; study
13. grew to be

DOWN

2. smart or intelligent
4. letters printed by machine
5. make unable to move
7. paper cover for mailing a letter
9. long, slender piece of wood
10. having courage

Part D

Choose the list or lists of words you want to learn. Then complete the activities next to each list you choose.

Match the clues and the review words.
1. the word used to answer *why*
2. something or someone liked best
3. a school of higher learning
4. a word that means "at last"

Review Words

finally
because
favorite
college

Unscramble the words that fit the definitions.
1. a large mass of snow rapidly sliding down the side of a mountain   *acelvnaha*
2. a mass of earth or rock sliding down a steep slope   *ddnesilla*
3. a long, deep, narrow valley eroded by running water   *rnivae*
4. a deep, narrow valley that is usually steep and rocky and has a stream   *eogrg*

Challenge Words

ravine
avalanche
gorge
landslide

Write a content word for each definition. Use the glossary.
1. atoms of the same element with different weights
2. to make impure by contact or to pollute
3. part of an atom that has a negative charge
4. particles given off by radioactive materials

Content Words

1. isotopes
2. contaminate
3. electron
4. radiation

Study Hint!

Remember to pronounce spelling words carefully and then spell them one syllable at a time.

31

THE VOWEL SOUNDS
/ü/ and /yü/

Part A

Say the words in the list below. Write the words.

1. crew
2. stewardess
3. maneuver
4. lieutenant
5. shoot
6. smooth
7. route
8. rumor
9. stupid
10. truth
11. tube
12. few
13. nephew
14. interview
15. humorous
16. junior
17. uniform
18. rescue
19. haiku *
20. whom *

All the words in the spelling list contain /ü/ or /yü/ as vowel sounds. These sounds have many spellings.

●Write the first list word in which /ü/ or /yü/ is spelled **ew, eu, ieu, oo, ou, u, u-e, iew, ue,** and **o.**

●Circle the two-letter spellings for /ü/ or /yü/.

∗Wild Words Words that end in **u** are usually words, like *haiku,* which are borrowed from another language.

The words *who* and *whom* are often confused. Use the word *whom* when it is **not** the subject of the sentence.

Choose list words to complete the story.

"We had a serious problem last night," the (1) s____s said in an (2) i____w after the (3) r____e.

"Our plane got lost in the blizzard and we got off our (4) r____e.

"A passenger started the (5) r____r that there was trouble. A (6) f____w people got very excited, and the (7) c____w had to work hard to calm them. A (8) l____t in (9) u____m asked his (10) n____w to play his guitar, and the (11) j____r passengers sang (12) h____s songs.

"Then the pilot, through a clever (13) m____r, made a (14) s____h landing in the snow.

"The excited passengers felt rather (15) s____d when they realized the (16) t____h, that we were safe."

17. Write the word that is pronounced /shüt/.

18. Write the word that is pronounced /tüb/ or /tyüb/.

19. Both wild words have the /ü/ sound. Write them.

20. Write the word that is pronounced /rüt/ or /rout/.

What's the Big Idea?

There are many ways to spell the sounds /ü/ or /yü/. Some of them are **ew, eu, ieu, oo, ou, u, u-e, iew, ue,** and **o.**

Proofreading

Find three words that must begin with capital letters in Bob's note. Write the words correctly.

Find six list words that are otherwise misspelled in the note. Write the words correctly.

There's a roomer that we won't have school on the wednesday before thanksgiving.

I got to intervue the mayor when he came to get his nefew monday. I did a stoopid thing when I called the mayor by the wrong name. A fue kids heard me. They thought it was humerous, but I didn't.

Handwriting

Start the letter **n** with an overhill stroke. Start the letter **u** with an uphill stroke. Write the words *junior* and *uniform*. Pay special attention to the letters **n** and **u**.

 # SPELLBOUND

Japanese haiku are about nature, often the seasons. Haiku contain three lines and do not rhyme. The first and third lines contain five syllables, and the second line contains seven. Read the haiku below and then write your own haiku.

Sun rising in East
Birds awaken to the light
A new day begins.

Part D

Choose the list or lists of words you want to learn. Then complete the activities next to each list you choose.

1. Write the two words that begin with **a** pronounced /ə/.
2. Write the contraction for *let us.*
3. Write the review words that mean:
   a. once more   b. many

again
against
lots
let's

Big Idea Words

1. Which two words at the right rhyme?
2. Use the other two words to answer these questions.
   a. What do you do at the end of a sentence?
   b. Which word means "to finish something"?
3. Which list word is an antonym of *senior?*

conclude
punctuate
cruel
fuel

Challenge Words

Write the challenge word for each clue or picture.
1. waterproofed canvas
2. mass of floating ice

kayak
iceberg
tarpaulin
caribou

3.

4.

Study Hint!

Pronounce your words carefully. Pay special attention to parts of words that have unusual spellings. Write the words and then check to see whether they are correct.

CONSONANT SOUNDS

Part A

Say the words in the list below. Write the words.

1. kneel
2. knowledge
3. knuckle
4. wrinkle
5. wrench
6. wrestled
7. debt
8. doubt
9. ghost
10. spaghetti
11. ghastly
12. plumber
13. bomb
14. hymn
15. autumn
16. calm
17. palm
18. rhyme
19. rhythm *
20. tomb *

Each word in this lesson contains two consonant letters together that stand for one sound.

● Write the words for which the pronunciations are given.
(nēl) (rench) (det) (gōst) (bom) (him) (päm) (rīm)

＊Wild Words   *Rhythm* refers to the regular repetition of a beat in music or poetry. Notice that the word *rhythm* contains two syllables but only one vowel letter.

A *tomb* is a grave. *Tomb* and *bomb* look as if they should rhyme, but the **o** in *tomb* stands for /ü/ as in *boom*.

1. Write the list words in which the patterns below appear at the beginning of a word or syllable.

   a. /n/ spelled **kn**   b. /r/ spelled **wr**

   c. /g/ spelled **gh**   d. /r/ spelled **rh**

2. Write the list words in which the patterns below appear at the end of a word or syllable.

   a. /t/ spelled **bt**   b. /m/ spelled **mn**

   c. /m/ spelled **mb**   d. /m/ spelled **lm**

3. Write the list word that goes with each picture.

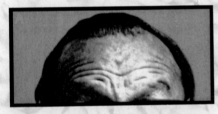

a

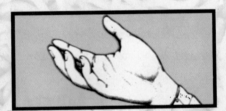

b

c

d

What's the Big Idea?

Sometimes two consonant letters together stand for the sound usually represented by just one of the letters.

Proofreading

Quotation marks are placed around the exact words
someone speaks. If the quoted words are at the beginning
of a sentence, a comma is placed after the words and before
the ending quotation marks. Correct three punctuation
errors below and write seven misspelled words.

It was dark when Tom and I left band practice. "Let's
cut through the cemetery, I suggested.

Tom seemed to have some dout about the idea, but
he agreed. Soon he whispered, "Listen to that gastly
rythm of metal beating on something.

He was sure it was a goste beating on a toom with a
rench, and he started to run.

The evening newscaster reported that a plummer
was repairing a broken water pipe in the cemetery.

Handwriting

_t   r   w_ Pay special attention to the beginning uphill strokes of **t**, **r**,
and **w** as you write *rhythm* and *wrestled*.

SPELLBOUND

Sometimes we use slang, an idiom, or figurative language
to express ideas. Use a list word in each idiom below.

Don't ____ under.

He's ____ with the problem.

She's in the ____ of his
hand.

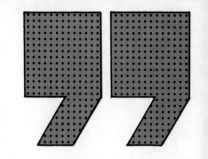

Choose the list or lists of words you want to learn. Then complete the activities next to each list you choose.

Review Words

1. Write the words that sound alike but have a different spelling and meaning from the words below.
   a. no   b. new
2. Write the review words that complete the question. __(a)__ were you born, and in __(b)__ state do you live now?

knew
know
which
where

Big Idea Words

1. Write the words that begin or end with the following consonant letters.
   a. **kn**   b. **wr**   c. **gh**   d. **mn**
2. Write the list word that looks somewhat like *ghetto.*

wreck
ghetto
knight
column

Content Words

Use the glossary to help you complete the puzzle.

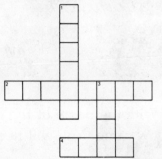

1. related to a system in which people worked for a lord in return for protection
2. a kingdom or empire
3. an emperor of Russia
4. a slave in a feudal system

czar 3
monarchy 2
serf 1
feudal 4

Study Hint!

Use the groupings of words under the headings in items 1 and 2 on page 37 to help you remember the two-letter consonant spellings for single consonant sounds.

WORDS FROM MANY LANGUAGES

Part A

Say the words in the list below. Write the words.

1. hamburger
2. sesame
3. mustard
4. pickle
5. cider
6. pastrami
7. caraway
8. shish kebab
9. steak
10. salad
11. taco
12. banana
13. booth
14. checkmate
15. polo
16. gong
17. ukulele
18. banjo
19. macramé *
20. jai alai *

● Write the name of the languages from which the words below came. You will need to use the glossary.

a. checkmate   b. polo   c. gong
d. ukulele   e. banjo   f. booth

✱Wild Words   *Jai alai* (hī′ ä lī′) is similar to handball. This Spanish compound word is written in two parts.

Some words borrowed from French have accent marks, as in *macramé*. The French got the word from the Turks, who often knotted fringe on a napkin (*makrama* in Turkish).

Part B

1. Write the name of the food that goes with each clue.
   a. ground beef patty named after Hamburg, Germany
   b. a word from Hebrew that now means "apple juice"
   c. a Romanian word, *pastrama*, for a smoked cut of beef
   d. seeds called *sesam* originally used for flavoring by Semitic people
   e. a seasoning used on meat and made from the seeds of a plant the French called *moustarde*
   f. fragrant, spicy seed that gets its name from the Arabic word *karawyā*
   g. several small pieces of meat roasted on sticks, from the Armenian words *shish kabab.*
   h. The French ate mixed raw vegetables with salt.
   i. Africans who spoke Mandingo gave us this fruit.
   j. The Norsemen would roast a slice of meat on a stick or stake.
   k. From Mexico comes meat wrapped in a thin, round cornmeal cake.
   l. The Dutch preserved a cucumber in vinegar, called a *pekel.*
2. Write three list words for musical instruments.
3. Write three list words related to games or sports.
4. Write the words that complete the sentence. Handicrafts such as (a) were displayed in a (b) .

What's the Big Idea?

When the English language borrows a word from another language, the spelling may or may not be changed to fit a common English spelling pattern.

Dictionary

sal ad (sal′əd), **1** raw, green vegetables, such as lettuce, cabbage, and celery, served with a dressing. Often cold meat, fish, eggs, cooked vegetables, or fruits are used along with, or instead of, the raw, green vegetables. **2** any green vegetable that can be eaten raw. [from Old French *salade* from Provencal *salada*, ultimately from Latin *sal* salt] *n.*
salad days, days of youthful inexperience.
salad dressing, sauce used in or on a salad.

An etymology begins with the source from which a word entered English and traces the history back to the earliest known source of the word. Look at the etymology, or history, of the word *salad. Salad* came into English from Old French. It entered French from Provençal. The people of Provence, a part of southeastern France once ruled by Rome, got their word *salada* from the Latin word *sal,* which meant "salt." Use the glossary to answer the questions that follow.

1. Was the word *sesame* first used in the Greek language or a Semitic language?
2. What language is the earliest known source of the word *checkmate?*
3. What word in the etymology of *polo* indicates that scholars are not sure of the origin of this word?

□ SPELLBOUND □

Write list words that can be used with all three of the words in each item. The first one is done for you.

a. *salad*	oil	dressing	fork
b. _____	player	strings	picker
c. _____	mill	jug	and doughnuts
d. _____	knife	sauce	sandwich
e. _____	jar	seeds	plaster
f. _____	split	cream pie	ice cream
g. _____	patty	steak	bun

Now write three words or phrases with which the word *sesame, booth,* or *polo* could be used.

Part D

Choose the list or lists of words you want to learn. Then complete the activities next to each list you choose.

Write the review word for each clue.

1. strange, very unusual
2. began
3. a water sport
4. at the same time

Review Words

swimming
while
weird
started

---

1. A pattern of checks and crosses in cloth is a plaid. Some Scottish Highlanders wear ____ clothing.
2. The French word *croche* means "hook," so to ____ is to do needlework with a hooked needle.
3. The ____ is a Japanese outer garment.
4. The *caftan* is an outer garment from Turkey. A choir robe may be a ____.

Big Idea Words

crochet
kimono
plaid
caftan

---

1. Bananas are grown mainly in the tropics, so they are known as a ____ fruit.
2. Use the glossary to match content words and definitions.
   a. a wind in the Indian Ocean and southeastern Asia
   b. the dried meat of the coconut
   c. a hardwood tree from Asia, used in shipbuilding

Content Words

copra
teak
monsoon
tropical

Study Hint!

Divide the list words into those that fit spelling patterns that you already know and those that must be memorized. Spend most of your time on the second group.

FINAL SYLLABLES WITH
/l/ AND /r/

Part A

Say the words in the list below. Write the words.

1. settle
2. handle
3. double
4. model
5. shovel
6. pistol
7. Capitol
8. carnival
9. council
10. popular
11. vinegar
12. later
13. panther
14. corner
15. harbor
16. honor
17. murmur
18. sulfur
19. ogre *
20. horror *

The sounds /əl/ and /l/ may be spelled **le** or with a vowel plus the letter **l**. The sound /ər/ is usually spelled with a vowel plus **r**.

● Write five spellings for /əl/ and /l/.
● Write the words that end with /ər/ spelled **ar** and **ur**.
● Circle all the letters that spell /ər/.

*Wild Words   Use this sentence to remember how to spell *horror*: **H**orrible **o**gres **r**ide **r**egularly **o**n **r**ailroads.

The **re** in *ogre* is like the **le** in *handle*. However, this pattern is far more common with **l** than with **r**.

Part B

Write the list words that fit the sentences below.

1. The _(a)_ crouched in the _(b)_ of the cage as the trainer cracked the whip.

2. _(a)_ and oil is a very _(b)_ salad dressing.

3. The captain gave his word of _(a)_ that he would not dump oil in the _(b)_ .

4. I heard the scientist _(a)_ , "I need more _(b)_ !"

5. The beautiful _(a)_ received so much fan mail, she had to _(b)_ it from her office.

6. I won't _(a)_ for a briefcase with a broken _(b)_ .

7. The evil _(a)_ made the children scream in _(b)_ .

8. Write the list word that fits each clue below.
   a. the opposite of *sooner*
   b. two times something
   c. an assembly or meeting
   d. a type of traveling show
   e. a handgun
   f. building in which Congress meets

What's the Big Idea?

The sounds /əl/ and /l/ may be spelled **le** or with a vowel plus the letter **l**. The sound /ər/ is usually spelled with a vowel plus **r**.

Proofreading

Remember that commas are used to separate the date from the year, and three or more things in a series. For example, grapes, apples, plums, and pears go on sale on June 1, 1978.

Read the letter below. Find six places where commas are needed and write each comma with the word or date after which it belongs. Then write the four misspelled words.

Dear Barry Bargainer,

We need your help to settel a dispite that we can't handel. Our company will not pay us doubel time or give us proper tools. We need hammers, nails, shovels and saws. We were supposed to have supplies by April 1, 1978 but did not get any.

Sincerely yours,

Ulysses Union

Handwriting

_ℓ t_ The letter l is looped at the top; the t is not. Cross the t in the middle. Practice by writing *Capitol*.

SPELLBOUND

Write the list word that belongs in this old saying: "You can catch more flies with honey than with ____." What does the saying mean?

Choose the list or lists of words you want to learn. Then complete the activities next to each list you choose.

	Big Idea Words
1. Write the words in which /əl/ is spelled **le**.	color
2. Write the word in which /ər/ is spelled as in:	locker
motor, doctor	angle
kicker, pitcher	triple

	Challenge Words
1. A synonym for *illness* that rhymes with *please* is ____.	disease
2. If something ails you, you have an ____.	ailment
3. If you are *not able* to do something, you have a ____.	disability
4. People who are unable to walk have a physical ____, but many handicapped people develop unusual talents.	handicap

---

	Content Words
Use the glossary to find the meaning of the content words.	linear
1. Write the adjective made from the word *line.*	reciprocal
2. Two numbers that when multiplied together equal 1, such as 4 and ¹⁄₄, are called ____ numbers.	hexagon
3. Label the illustrations.	pyramid

a.   b.

Study Hint!

When you hear /ər/ or /əl/ in a word, look carefully at the spelling. Group the list words in any way that will help you remember the correct spellings.

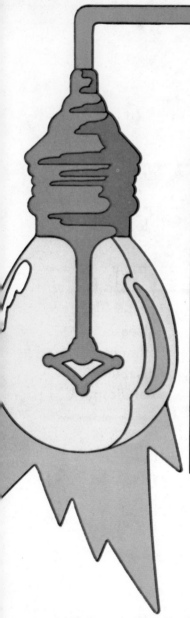

REVIEW

Here are some steps to help you study your words.

Before you write each word:
  Look at the word.
  Look at the letters.
  Say the word.
  Listen to the sounds.
When you write each word:
  Copy the word from your list.
  Write the word without looking at it.
After you write each word:
  Check the word with your list.
  Did you make a mistake?
  Notice where you made the mistake and begin
    the steps again.

Write the five review words for each lesson. Did you remember to record your misspelled or most troublesome words after the lesson test? If you forgot, write any you think of now under the heading Personal Words.

Lesson 7: More Spellings for /ā/, /ī/, /ō/, and /ē/

Review Words	**Personal Words**
1. paralyze	1. _____
2. envelope	2. _____
3. magazine	3. _____
4. furnace✱	4. _____
5. skis✱	5. _____

Lesson 8: The Vowel Sounds /ü/ and /yü/

Review Words	Personal Words
1. stupid	1. _____
2. humorous	2. _____
3. uniform	3. _____
4. haiku*	4. _____
5. whom*	5. _____

Lesson 9: Consonant Sounds

Review Words	Personal Words
1. knowledge	1. _____
2. doubt	2. _____
3. spaghetti	3. _____
4. rhythm*	4. _____
5. tomb*	5. _____

Lesson 10: Words from Many Languages

Review Words	Personal Words
1. hamburger	1. _____
2. mustard	2. _____
3. banana	3. _____
4. macramé*	4. _____
5. jai alai*	5. _____

Lesson 11: Final Syllables with /l/ and /r/

Review Words	Personal Words
1. model	1. _____
2. carnival	2. _____
3. popular	3. _____
4. ogre*	4. _____
5. horror*	5. _____

1. Write the five words that contain the sound /ər/ in the final syllable.

2. Write the two words that are paper products.

3. Write the three words that are associated with sports or hobbies.

4. Write the four words that name things you can eat.

5. Write the word that means the opposite of each word or phrase below.

   a. to be certain   b. ignorance   c. not well liked

   d. to make powerful   e. sad   f. kind person

6. Write the word that means the same or almost the same as each word or phrase below.

   a. burial place   b. foolish   c. special clothing

   d. amusement place   e. heater   f. kind of poetry

   g. small copy   h. which person   i. musical beat

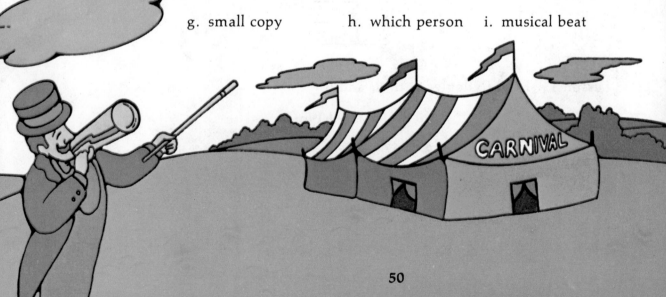

50

7. Use each group of words in a sentence. Make the sentences as funny as you wish; they can be downright silly like the one below.

   a. carnival, uniform, mustard   *The carnival barker asked the hot-dog man if mustard were part of his uniform.*

   b. spaghetti, hamburger, banana

   c. humorous, magazine, popular

   d. haiku, rhythm, model

   e. skis, furnace, horror

Test Yourself
Find the misspelled word in each group. Then write the word correctly.

1. a. paralyze   b. magazine
   c. envelop   d. skis

2. a. haiku   b. whom
   c. stupid   d. humurous

3. a. knowlege   b. tomb
   c. doubt   d. spaghetti

4. a. hamburger   b. bananna
   c. jai alai   d. macramé

5. a. popular   b. carnival
   c. model   d. oger

Personal Words
Write your personal words in three groups: (1) any words that contain the sound /ər/, (2) words that contain one consonant sound spelled with two different consonant letters as in to*mb*, (3) all other words.

COMPOUND WORDS

Part A

Say the words in the list below. Write the words.

1. anyway
2. oatmeal
3. nearby
4. yourself
5. downstairs
6. upstairs
7. soap opera
8. barbed wire
9. string beans
10. living room
11. sleeping bag
12. blue jay
13. brother-in-law
14. sisters-in-law
15. play-offs
16. worn-out
17. old-fashioned
18. twenty-one
19. nothing*
20. marshmallow*

Words 1–6 are *closed* compound words, words 7–12 are *open* compound words, and words 13–18 are *hyphenated* compound words.

● Write the first two closed compound words.
● Write the first two open compound words.
● Write the first hyphenated compound word.

✳Wild Words   The word *nothing* (nuth′ing) is a compound of *no* and *thing*. The word *marshmallow* (märsh′mal′ō) is a compound of *marsh* and *mallow*. Write the wild words.

1. The marsh mallow is a plant. Its roots were once used for making sweets. Write the wild word we use today for this sweet candy.

2. Write the wild word which is a compound of *no* and *thing.*

3. Write the other six words that are closed compounds.

4. Write the six words that are open compound words.

5. Write the six words that are hyphenated compounds.

6. Note that in some hyphenated compound words the plural is formed by adding *-s* in different places. Write the plural list word in which *-s* was added to the first word, *sister,* and the plural list word in which *-s* was added to the last word, *off.*

7. Which three words name foods?

8. Write the two closed compounds that are opposites.

What's the Big Idea?

Closed compound words are written as one word. Open compound words have a space between words. Hyphenated compound words have a hyphen between words.

Dictionary

Remember that some words have more than one stressed syllable. The syllable with the stronger stress gets the darker, or *primary* (ˈ), accent. A syllable that is also stressed, but less strongly, gets a *secondary* (ˈ) accent.

The words below are divided into syllables. Say each word, noticing where the stress falls. Write the words in syllables and put the accent marks after the stressed syllable or syllables. Use the glossary to check your answers.

1. (nuth ing)   2. (up sterz)   3. (en ē wā)
4. (ōt mēl)   5. (märsh mal ō)

Handwriting

uro ura

In writing the letter **w** next to **a** or **o**, note how the sidestroke on **w** joins the top of the **o** or **a**. The **w** never returns to the line before connecting to the next letter. Practice writing *anyway* and *worn-out*.

⬜ SPELLBOUND ⬜

By changing one word in a compound it is possible to make a new compound word. For example, the open compound word *string beans* could be changed to *lima beans, green beans,* or *pinto beans.* Change the first word in the following compounds and make as many new compounds as you can: *sleeping bag, yourself, living room,* and *anyway.*

Part D

Choose the list or lists of words you want to learn.
Then complete the activities next to each list you choose.

Write the words that mean the opposite of the words
below.
1. a few
2. outside
3. not satisfactory
4. inside

Review Words

inside
outside
a lot
all right

Write the words that follow the same pattern as:
1. father-in-law
2. looker-on
3. outlook
4. bill of rights

Big Idea Words

bill of sale
outrage
passer-by
son-in-law

---

1. Write the challenge word that was made from each base
   word.
   a. achieve
   b. accomplish
2. Write the words that complete the sentences.
   a. The women completed the business agreement, or
      ____, late Tuesday.
   b. Some businesses take unfair advantage of, or ____,
      workers in less developed nations of the world.

Challenge Words

exploit
achievement
accomplishment
transaction

Study Hint!

Write each word. Then cover it and write the word
again. Pay special attention to whether it is an open,
closed, or hyphenated compound.

55

CONTRACTIONS AND POSSESSIVES

Part A

Say the words in the list below. Write the words.

1. *hadn't*
2. *hasn't*
3. *haven't*
4. *he'd*
5. *she'd*
6. *we'd*
7. *you'd*
8. *they'd*
9. *they'll*
10. *they've*

11. *children's*
12. *grandfather's*
13. *chef's*
14. *neighbor's*
15. *neighbors'*
16. *sister's*
17. *sisters'*
18. *daughter's*
19. *cheeseburger* ✱
20. *smog* ✱

a. his _____ cat

b. his _____ cat

c. the _____ cat

● Words are put together to form contractions, and apostrophes show where letters are left out in list words _____ to _____.

● In possessives, apostrophes show ownership. Study the pictures and write the number of the list word that completes each phrase.

✱**Wild Words**   Each wild word is a blend of two other words with letters left out. Blends have no apostrophes.

● Circle the letters to be left out; then write the blends.

cheese and hamburger   smoke and fog

Part B

1. Write the list words described below.

   a. five words with contractions for *had* or *would*
   b. three words with contractions for *not*
   c. one word with the contraction for *will*
   d. one word with the contraction for *have*
   e. five singular possessives, like *girl's* or *man's*
   f. three plural possessives, like *girls'* or *men's*
   g. the blend made from *smoke* and *fog*
   h. the blend made from *cheese* and *hamburger*

2. Write the list word that best completes each sentence.

   a. The teacher corrected the ____ workbooks.
   b. Joan likes to keep her two next-door ____ dogs.
   c. A customer asked the waitress for the ____ recipe for cream puffs.
   d. Tom ____ any pencils today.
   e. The children decided to go to the museum because ____ been to the zoo several times.

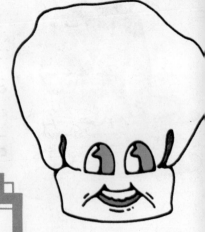

What's the Big Idea?

Possessive nouns and contractions contain apostrophes.
In contractions, apostrophes mark places where letters
are left out. In possessives, apostrophes show ownership.

Proofreading

In writing, contractions and possessives show the quick, natural way we often talk. It seems more natural to say *haven't* than *have not,* though both are correct. It's easier to say *my sister's friend* than *the friend of my sister.*

Read the paragraph below. Write six misspelled words correctly. If apostrophes are left out of contractions and possessives, the words are misspelled.

Youd love our nieghbors cabin. It was an old barn that hadnt been used for years. Outside it still looks like a barn, but inside thayve changed it. The kitchen is where the cows used to be. Their dauthers room is in the loft. Mr. Sims says that hed like to retire there.

SPELLBOUND

Someone created the word *smog* from *smoke* and *fog.* In a similar way, a weather forecaster might say that snow and cold combined is *snold* weather. Write blends that could be used in the blanks below.

1. Snow and freezing weather is ____ weather.
2. Snow when it is almost clear is ____ weather.
3. Breezy and rainy weather is ____.
4. Mixed snow and rain is ____.

Try making up your own words using weather terms like *snow, flurry, drizzle, windy, rain, breezy, chilly, cold, freezing, thunder,* and *storm.*

Part D

Choose the list or lists of words you want to learn.
Then complete the activities next to each list you choose.

---

1. Write the review words that complete the sentences.

   Upon seeing the injured man and woman, Mr. and
Mrs. Hill stopped their car. When the police came, the Hills
said, " (a) glad (b) here. We (c) know who hit these
people, but (d) seriously hurt and need help."

2. Write an ending for the story-beginning above.

Review Words

you're

we're

they're

don't

---

1. Which two possessives refer to people?

2. Rewrite the following sentence, using a possessive.
   The population of the world is over four billion.

3. Which word is a contraction?

4. Which list word follows the pattern of *women's?*

Big Idea Words

salesman's

world's

women's

wouldn't

Use the number clues to match the content words with the
sentences in which the context defines them.

   The passing of characteristics, or (1) , from parents to
their young through genes is known as (2) . The
strongest, or (3) , genes determine the sex and other traits
of the young. The study of genes is (4) .

Content Words

1. traits
2. heredity
3. dominant
4. genetics

Study Hint!

Write each word. Check to see that you've left the
correct letters out. Make sure the apostrophe is in the
right place. Then write the word again.

59

This crayon is about one decimeter long.

This insect is about one centimeter long.

TERMS OF MEASUREMENT

Part A

Say the words in the list below. Write the words.

1. centimeter
2. decameter
3. millimeter
4. kilometer
5. meter
6. hectoliter
7. kiloliter
8. centiliter
9. milliliter
10. liter

11. milligram
12. kilogram
13. gram
14. furlong
15. dram
16. ounce
17. bushel
18. metric ton
19. linear*
20. liquid*

A roller skate weighs about one kilogram.

A *meter* is a measure of length, a *gram* is a unit of weight, and a *liter* is a measure of volume.

● Write the first two words that measure length.
● Write the first two words that express weight.
● Write the first two words that measure volume.

*Wild Words   *Liquid* comes from a Latin word that means "fluid." Measurements that deal with the volume of fluids are made in *liquid measures.*

Line is the base word of *linear,* which refers to length.

The metric system is easy if you learn these forms.

deca = 10　　　　　　　　hecto = 100　　　　　　　　kilo = 1000

deci = .1 (1/10) of a　　　centi = .01 (1/100) of a　　milli = .001 (1/1000) of a

1. A milligram is 1/1000 gram; a _____ is 1000 grams.

2. Complete the chart of metric measures.

Weight Grams		Volume (liquid or dry) Liters		Linear or Length Meters	
1000	_kilogram_	1000	(c)	1000	(h)
100	hectogram	100	(d)	100	hectometer
10	decagram	10	decaliter	10	(i)
1	(a)	1	(e)	1	(j)
.1	decigram	.1	deciliter	.1	decimeter
.01	centigram	.01	(f)	.01	(k)
.001	(b)	.001	(g)	.001	(l)

3. Use list words 14-20 to complete these sentences. You may use the glossary or a dictionary if necessary.

We use (a) measures for milk and use dry measures like (b) for wheat.

A meter is an example of (c) measure.

A (d) or *drachm* is ⅛ of an ounce.

Inch and (e) come from the Latin word *uncia*.

The Old English words for "furrow" and "long" were combined to make (f) , the word for ⅛ of a mile.

You would need a truck to hold a (g) .

This paper clip weighs about one gram.

What's the Big Idea?

In the metric system, *meter* measures length, *gram* weight, and *liter* volume. Combining forms, like *milli-*, that end with the letter **i** are fractions, or less than one.

hat, āge, fär;
let, ēqual, tėrm;
it, īce; hot, ōpen, ôrder;
oil, out; cup, pút, rüle;
ch, child; ng, long; sh, she;
th, thin; ŦH, then;
zh, measure;

ə represents *a* in about,
e in taken, *i* in pencil,
o in lemon, *u* in circus.

Part C

Dictionary

The space between the parts of an entry word shows where the word may be broken at the end of a writing line. The spaces between the pronunciation symbols help you pronounce a word. The word breaks may be different, as in **sneak er** (snē′kər).

Look at the pronunciations in the paragraph below and then find the words in the glossary. Write each word as you would divide it at the end of a line. Show each place a word may be divided.

The (1) (sü′pər in ten′dənt) is learning metric measures for his (2) (biz′nis). He's pouring a (3) (brou′nish) (4) (lik′wid) in a (5) (lē′tər) bottle. Next he is going to learn (6) (lin′ē ər) measures and compare a (7) (dek′ə mē tər) with a (8) (kə lom′ə tər).

Handwriting

g   q   o

The letters **g**, **q**, and **o** are closed letters. Write *liquid* and *kilogram*. Pay special attention to **g**, **q**, and **o** so they won't be confused with **y**, **u**, and **a**.

☐ SPELLBOUND ☐

Write the answer to each question below.
1. Would candy bars be labeled in grams or liters?
2. Would you run in a 500-meter or 500-liter dash?
3. Would you rather have a decigram or decagram of gold?
4. Would you buy rope by the meter or liter?

Part D

Choose the list or lists of words you want to learn.
Then complete the activities next to each list you choose.

Write the review word that means the same as each clue.

Review Words

1. frightening
2. most of the time
3. very likely
4. truly, for real

probably
really
scary
usually

All the words in this list begin with a prefix meaning "not."
Write the word that means:

Challenge Words

1. has no sense or logic
2. is not practical
3. not able or capable
4. not likely or probable

incapable
impractical
improbable
illogical

---

1. Write a content word for each base word.
   a. exaggerate   b. narrate
2. Write the compound word that is formed with the words *flash* and *back.*
3. Write the word that begins with /k/.

Content Words

flashback
exaggeration
characterization
narrative

Study Hint!

Study metric terms separately from the traditional measurements. Although metric terms are much longer, they are easy to spell once you learn each part.

63

UNUSUAL SPELLINGS FOR /ē/ AND /ô/

Part A

Say the words in the list below. Write the words.

1. ceiling
2. protein
3. leisure
4. eerie
5. prairie
6. wiener
7. yield
8. receive
9. deceive
10. seize
11. believe
12. pieces
13. niece
14. siege
15. already
16. altogether
17. scald
18. chalk
19. foreign *
20. frontier *

The sound /ē/ can be spelled **ei, ie, ie-e,** or **ei-e.**
● Write the first list word for each spelling.

The sound /ô/ can be spelled with the letter **a** before an **l** as in *salt.* Sometimes the letters **al** together spell the sound /ô/ as in *talk.*
● Write the first list word in which /ô/ is spelled **a** and **al.**
● Circle the letters that spell /ô/ in the list words.

＊Wild Words   In *foreign* and *frontier* **ei** and **ie** do not stand for /ē/.

Part B

1. Write four words in which /ē/ is spelled **ie**.

2. Write four words that contain /ē/ spelled **ie-e**.

3. Write three words in which /ô/ is spelled **a**.

4. Write the word in which /ô/ is spelled **al**.

5. Write three words that contain /ē/ spelled **ei-e**.

6. Write three words in which /ē/ is spelled **ei**.

7. Write the two wild words in which the letters **ei** and **ie** do not stand for /ē/.

8. When a consonant between two vowels follows a short vowel, as in *kilogram,* the word is usually divided after the consonant. When a consonant between two vowels follows a long vowel, as in *protein,* the word is usually divided before the consonant. For example, *kilogram,* which has the short /i/, is divided after the **l** *(kil-ogram).* *Protein* has a long /ō/. Where would it be divided?

Proofreading

In plural possessives, the apostrophe (') usually goes after the **s.** Find three words that need apostrophes. Find four list words that are misspelled. Write the words correctly.

My three brothers children went on a weiner roast last night. After they ate, Uncle Joe told them a story about a fronteir town on the prarie. He told them what a hard life the people had and how cold the peoples houses were. Hearing the coyotes howls in the night, just as the homesteaders did, gave the children an erie feeling.

Handwriting

i   e   Both **i** and **e** begin with uphill strokes. The letter **e** is looped, but **i** is not. Make sure you put the dot directly over the **i.** Write the words *ceiling* and *eerie.*

 **SPELLBOUND**

In some parts of the country a *hot dog* is called a *wiener.* In other places it's called a *frank.*

Below are some words that are scrambled up. Put the words that mean the same thing into three groups.
Hint: Read all the words first.

flapjack	sofa	davenport
soda	hotcake	soft drink
pop	couch	pancake

Choose the list or lists of words you want to learn.
Then complete the activities next to each list you choose.

---

1. Write the word that follows each pattern for /ē/.

   field   niece   deceit

2. Write the word that means "to change."
3. Write a list word that rhymes with *retrieve.*

Big Idea Words
relief
retrieve
conceit
alter

Write the words that mean the opposite of the underlined words.
1. It is the truth; there is no ____.
2. Proceed immediately; there will be no ____.
3. I was favorable to the idea; he was ____ to it.
4. It is unlikely to rain; it is ____ to sleet.

Challenge Words
1. deceit
2. reprieve
3. adverse
4. liable

---

1. Write labels for the pictured objects.

2. Two types of materials for drawing or painting are (a)
   and (b) paint.

Content Words
easel
tempera
charcoal
palette

Study Hint!

Group your list words according to spelling patterns for
specific sounds. Study the words in each group together.

THE CONSONANT SOUND /j/

Part A

Say the words in the list below. Write the words.

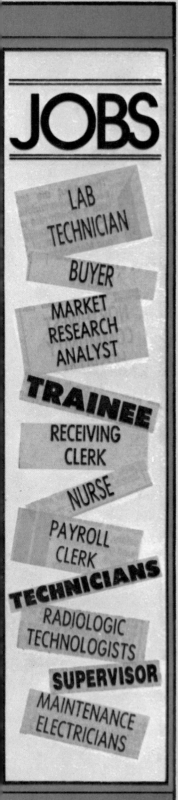

1. gently
2. geranium
3. gigantic
4. original
5. suggest
6. junction
7. jazz
8. jobs
9. major
10. budget
11. fledgling
12. gadget
13. midget
14. badge
15. edge
16. bridge
17. dodge
18. judge
19. acknowledgment*
20. education*

The sound /j/ is spelled **j** or **g** at the beginning or in the middle of a word, but usually **dg** only in the middle of a word and **dge** at the end of a word.

- Write the first two words in which /j/ is spelled **g**.
- Write the first two words in which /j/ is spelled **dg**.
- Write the first two words in which /j/ is spelled **dge**.
- Underline the letters that spell /j/ in list words 1–10.

*Wild Words   The sound /j/ is spelled **dge** in *acknowledge*, but **dg** in *acknowledgment*. The letter **d** spells the sound /j/ in *education*.

Part B

1. Write five words in which /j/ is spelled **g.**

2. Write five words in which /j/ is spelled **dg.**

3. Write five words in which /j/ is spelled **dge.**

4. Write four words in which /j/ is spelled **j.**

5. Write the wild word which means "training."

6. Use a list word for something you would be likely to find in each of the places below.
   a. in a flower shop
   b. on a uniform
   c. in a nightclub
   d. in a courthouse
   e. over a river

SINGLE GERANIUM

What's the Big Idea?

The sound /j/ is spelled **j** or **g** at the beginning or in the middle of a word, but usually **dg** only in the middle of a word and **dge** at the end of a word.

COURAGE?

Part C
Dictionary

To help you find out how a word is spelled, many dictionaries have a spelling table which shows the different ways certain sounds can be represented.

Looking up the different ways the consonant and vowel sounds in a word can be spelled will help you imagine how the word itself might be spelled. Look up each possibility until you find the word in the dictionary. You probably won't have to try all of the possibilities because the spelling table lists the more common spellings first and the rarer spellings last.

1. Use the spelling table and the glossary to write the correct spellings for the words listed below.
   a. (kōl′rä′bē)   b. (ə kil′ēz)

SPELLBOUND

The word *acknowledgment* has 14 letters. How many new words can you make by using these letters? Each word must have at least four letters. No letter may be used more than once in a word unless it appears in *acknowledgment* more than once, as the letters **e** and **n** do.

Score: 20 or more —excellent
15 to 19   —good
10 to 14   —fair
less than 10—need practice

Here are some words to get you started:
gentle   lodge   towel

_70_   *Part C Score:* _____ —22_

Part D

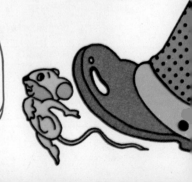

Choose the list or lists of words you want to learn.
Then complete the activities next to each list you choose.

Review Words

1. Write the two words that are contractions.
2. Write another word for "till."
3. Which word means "on"?

that's

I'm

upon

until

Big Idea Words

1. Write the word that fits each pair of phrases.
   a window ＿＿, a mountain ＿＿
   a door ＿＿, a gate ＿＿
2. Write the word that means the same as these words.
   a. to hurt, to wound
   b. bravery, fearlessness

hinge

courage

injure

ledge

Content Words

In, over, and *under* may be used as prepositions.
Yet, but, and *after* may be used as conjunctions.
Oh! Ouch! and *Well!* may be used as interjections.
Kind, big, and *bright* may be used as adjectives.

interjection

conjunction

preposition

adjective

Write the content word that describes how each numbered
word is used in the sentence.
(1) *After* the (2) *big* boy jumped (3) *over* the fence, he
yelled, (4) *"Ouch!* I think I broke my leg."

Study Hint!

Study the list words in small groups that have the
sound /j/ spelled the same way. Break long words into
smaller parts to make them easier to study.

71

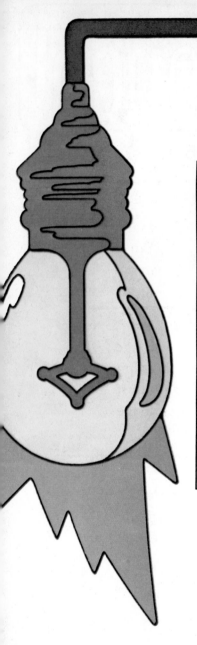

REVIEW

Here are some steps to help you study your words.

Before you write each word:
    Look at the word.
    Look at the letters.
    Say the word.
    Listen to the sounds.
When you write each word:
    Copy the word from your list.
    Write the word without looking at it.
After you write each word:
    Check the word with your list.
    Did you make a mistake?
    Notice where you made the mistake and begin
      the steps again.

Write the five review words for each lesson. Did you remember to record your misspelled or most troublesome words after each lesson test? If you forgot, write any you think of now under the heading Personal Words.

Lesson 13: Compound Words

Review Words	Personal Words
1. nearby	1. _____
2. downstairs	2. _____
3. play-offs	3. _____
4. nothing*	4. _____
5. marshmallow*	5. _____

Lesson 14: Contractions and Possessives

Review Words	Personal Words
1. haven't	1. _____
2. children's	2. _____
3. neighbor's	3. _____
4. cheeseburger*	4. _____
5. smog*	5. _____

Lesson 15: Terms of Measurement

Review Words	Personal Words
1. millimeter	1. _____
2. kilometer	2. _____
3. ounce	3. _____
4. linear*	4. _____
5. liquid*	5. _____

Lesson 16: Unusual Spellings for /ē/ and /ô/

Review Words	Personal Words
1. prairie	1. _____
2. believe	2. _____
3. niece	3. _____
4. foreign*	4. _____
5. frontier*	5. _____

Lesson 17: The Consonant Sound /j/

Review Words	Personal Words
1. gigantic	1. _____
2. badge	2. _____
3. edge	3. _____
4. acknowledgment*	4. _____
5. education*	5. _____

1. Write the word that means nearly the opposite of:
   a. far-off b. upstairs c. everything
   d. have e. solid f. native

2. Write the word that rhymes with:
   a. ledge b. scary c. receive
   d. bounce e. log f. piece

3. Write two words that name foods.

4. Write two words that are possessives.

5. Write five words that contain the sound /j/.

6. Write the word that means:
   a. outside one's own country (fôr'ən)
   b. extra games to settle a tie (plā'ôfs')
   c. unsettled part of a country (frun tir')

7. Write the words that complete the sentences.
   A measure of length is __(a)__ measure. (lin'ē ər)
   In the metric system a __(b)__ and a __(c)__ are linear
   measures. (kə lom'ə tər *or* kil'ə mē'tər), (mil'ə mē'tər)

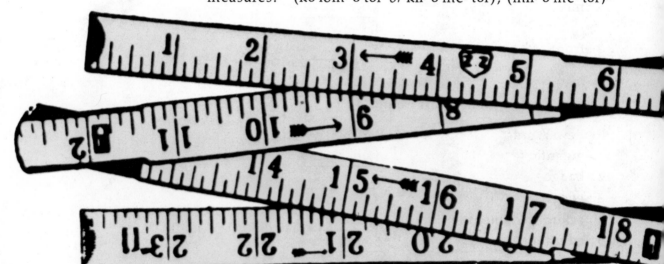

Use the clues on the right to complete the puzzle below.

ACROSS
1. opposite of *native*
4. 1,000 meters
6. huge
7. daughter of one's sister or brother

DOWN
2. where something ends
3. unsettled part of a country
5. 1/16th of a pound *or* 1/16th of a pint

Test Yourself
Write the misspelled word in each group correctly.

1. a. nearby   b. downstairs
   c. nothing   d. marshmellow

2. a. children's   b. neighbor's
   c. have'nt   d. smog

3. a. millameter   b. ounce
   c. linear   d. liquid

4. a. niece   b. beleive
   c. foreign   d. frontier

5. a. badge   b. education
   c. gigentic   d. edge

Personal Words
Make up a crossword puzzle using your personal words.
Add any words you need to make the puzzle work.

WORDS WITH LATIN PREFIXES

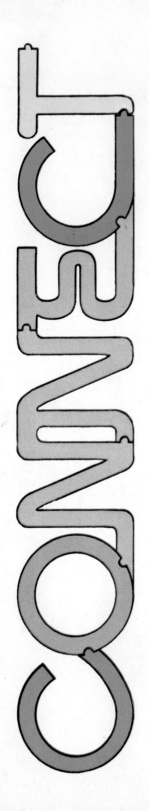

Part A

Say the words in the list below. Write the words.

1. comfortable
2. commercial
3. committee
4. communicate
5. compare
6. compete
7. concert
8. congress
9. connect
10. conservation
11. constitution
12. contest
13. collaborate
14. collapse
15. collide
16. coexist
17. coincidence
18. cooperate
19. condominium *
20. coalition *

In Latin *com-, con-, col-,* and *co-* all mean "with."
● With what three letters do words 1–6 begin?
● With what three letters do words 7–12 begin?
● With what three letters do words 13–15 begin?
● With what two letters do words 16–18 begin?

✳Wild Words   In a *condominium* each family owns its living space but shares some things *with* other owners.

A *coalition* is a temporary union of groups working *with* one another to achieve a common purpose.

Part B

1. A great many decisions are made in the United States Congress, and representatives and senators use many of the list words. Write list words for the pronunciations given in parentheses.

   a. "This bill needs more study. Let's send it back to a (kə mit′ē) for discussion."

   b. "Unless we send more food, many people will starve and the government will (kə laps′)."

   c. "Although we disagree with a nation, it can exist and so can we. We must (kō′ig zist′) peacefully."

   d. "Mr. Chairman, I'd feel more (kum′fər tə bəl) with a stronger (kon′sər vā′shən) bill to clean up our air and water."

   e. "Members of (kon′gris) need to (kə myü′nə kāt) the importance of this law to the voters."

   f. "The (kon′stə tü′shən) of our country gives us the power to make a law regulating (kə mėr′shəl) vehicles traveling between states."

   g. "Let's not make this a (kon′test) in which we (kəm pēt′) with other nations. Let's work together. Let's (kə lab′ə rāt′) to put a person on Mars."

2. Write the word that means about the opposite of each word or phrase below.

   a. planned event
   b. disconnect
   c. avoid hitting
   d. contrast
   e. compete
   f. solo

3. Write the wild words.

What's the Big Idea?

Many English words that came from Latin begin with the letters **com**, **con**, **col**, and **co**.

Part C

Proofreading

Notice that colons are used below to separate hours from minutes and to mark the beginning of a listing.

The game starts at 7:30 P.M.

Bring your materials: paper, ruler, and two pencils.

Copy the figures or words where colons are missing and add the colons. Write five misspelled words correctly.

CONSURVATION WEEKEND TRIP!

Comunicate these facts to your family We leave school Friday at 400 P.M. We return Sunday between 2.30 and 4.30 P.M.

You must bring these items   compass, sleeping bag, toothbrush, canteen, and dried food. Also bring hiking clothes, thick socks, sturdy comterble shoes, jacket, and rain parka.

Please cooporate and be ready on time.

Field Trip Comittee

SPELLBOUND

Read the tongue twister below fast. Then write another tongue twister, using list words or forms of list words.

The car carrying the conservation committee collided with a cart that had collapsed near a condominium.

78   *Part C Score:* _____ —11

Part D

Choose the list or lists of words you want to learn.
Then complete the activities next to each list you choose.

Review Words

1. Write the words that have these base words:
   busy   pass

2. Write the word that has /s/ spelled **c** and also **ss.**

3. Write the word that means "time gone by."

business
passed
past
necessary

Challenge Words

Unscramble the letters to match the definitions.
1. sweater with a high collar (klrteeutcn)
2. Mexican shawl (rpseae)
3. knitted or crocheted blanket or shawl (gfahna)
4. sweater that buttons down the front (dinragca)

cardigan
afghan
turtleneck
serape

Content Words

1. The prefix *co-* means "together" or "with"; so operating together, or working together, shows ____.

2. Use the glossary as you complete the sentences.
   Lessons in social studies often tell about a struggle, or _(a)_ , between nations. Sometimes quarreling over borders can cause a _(b)_ . Other countries that refuse to take sides are called _(c)_ .

neutral
conflict
cooperation
dispute

Study Hint!

If you hear only one consonant sound after *co-*, double the consonant when you spell the word: *collaborate, committee,* and *connect.*

MORE WORDS WITH LATIN PREFIXES

Part A

Say the words in the list below. Write the words.

1. decent	11. subscribe
2. declaration	12. substitute
3. defense	13. subtract
4. described	14. superintendent
5. develop	15. supernatural
6. disastrous	16. supersonic
7. disguised	17. surface
8. distract	18. surplus
9. distress	19. surprise *
10. distributed	20. surrounded *

- Write the first two words that begin with *de-*.
- Write the first two words that begin with *dis-*.
- Write the first two words that begin with *sub-*.
- Write the last two words that begin with *super-*.
- Circle the Latin prefixes in words 1–10.

*Wild Words   *Surprise* means "without warning."
Surrounded means "shut in on all sides." To help you spell
these words, note that in *surprise* the second syllable is
spelled **p-r-i-s-e**, not **p-r-i-z-e**, and think of *sur-* + *rounded*
when you spell *surrounded*.

Test Score: _____ —20   **80**   Part A Score: _____ —18

Part B

1. When a word begins with a prefix, such as *super-,* the best place to divide it is before the base word. Write the words *supersonic, supernatural,* and *superintendent* with a hyphen to show where you would divide each.

2. Read the sentences below. Write the correct word for each sentence from the groups of words at the right.

If you declare something, you've made a (a) .

Sam likes to (b) his own pictures.

A (c) wage is one that is fair.

One (d) against the flu is inoculation.

Bea told about the play and (e) each scene.

decent
declaration
defense
described
develop

Tino went to the party (f) as a horse.

It's not just bad; it's (g) .

The charities (h) food to all the poor.

A ship in trouble would send (i) signals.

Your mumbling certainly does (j) me.

disastrous
disguised
distract
distress
distributed

Do you (k) to any magazines?

He said I couldn't (l) French fries for grits.

The minus sign means (m) .

subscribe
substitute
subtract

The smooth (n) of the old road was a (o) .

The storekeeper was (p) by a (q) of toys.

surface
surplus
surprise
surrounded

What's the Big Idea?

Many words that came from Latin and related languages begin with the letters **de, dis, sub, super,** and **sur.**

Part C

Dictionary

up in the air
look alive
up in arms
drum up
keep your head
bury the hatchet
beat around
   the bush
buckle down to

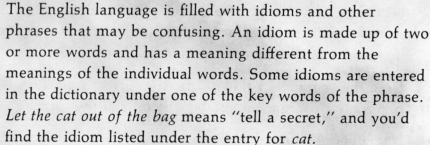

The English language is filled with idioms and other phrases that may be confusing. An idiom is made up of two or more words and has a meaning different from the meanings of the individual words. Some idioms are entered in the dictionary under one of the key words of the phrase. *Let the cat out of the bag* means "tell a secret," and you'd find the idiom listed under the entry for *cat*.

Fit the appropriate idioms in the sentences below. You may have to look up the meanings in a dictionary. Remember to look under the most important word first.

1. "Say what you mean, and don't ____."
2. The plans for a new library are still ____.
3. I was ____ when my vacation was canceled.
4. "____; don't dawdle!"
5. The sales manager decided to ____ business by advertising in the newspaper.
6. In times of distress it's hard to ____.
7. The feuding families decided to ____.
8. Every new year Ron resolves to ____ his studies.

Handwriting

_b f_

The letters **b** and **f** have tall loops. Write *surface* and *subscribe* to practice **b** and **f**.

SPELLBOUND

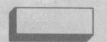

You may wish to keep a list of idioms. Be sure to check the meanings before you use them—or you may "come a cropper."

Part D

Choose the list or lists of words you want to learn.
Then complete the activities next to each list you choose.

Review Words

1. Write the review word that follows this pattern.
   famous, generous
2. Which two words begin their second syllables with consonant blends?
3. Fit the word in the pattern below.
   unicycle, _____, tricycle

bicycle
afraid
control
humorous

Big Idea Words

1. Which word is a three-word compound?
2. Which two words have double consonant letters?
3. In a Demolition Derby the object is to _____ old cars.
4. Write a list word in the pattern of *surpass*.

disappoint
demolish
surpass
superhighway

Challenge Words

Use your glossary to find the correct challenge word for each blank below.

   The (1) conditions on the ship threw the (2) crew into a state of (3) . If things didn't improve quickly, some of them were even thinking of (4) .

disgruntled
haphazard
treachery
turmoil

Study Hint!

Study carefully the list words with which you had difficulty.
Choose as many as you can and make a crossword puzzle.
Trade puzzles with a classmate.

HOMOPHONES

Part A

Say the words in the list below. Write the words.

1. board
2. bored
3. heard
4. herd
5. main
6. mane
7. some
8. sum
9. sent
10. cent

11. ate
12. eight
13. waist
14. waste
15. wait
16. weight
17. weak
18. week
19. ware *
20. wear *

Homophones are words that are pronounced the same, but have different meanings and usually have different spellings.

● Write a homophone for *board, waist, herd, mane, week,* and *some.*

✱Wild Words   *Where* is not usually considered a homophone for *wear* and *ware,* but the three words are pronounced alike in some places and are often confused. The word *ware* is most frequently seen in compounds such as *hardware, warehouse,* and *silverware.*

Part B

Write the correct homophone from the list words to complete each sentence. The homophones are in pairs.

1. I get _____ watching television.
2. I love to jump off a diving _____.
3. Have you _____ about John?
4. He bought a _____ of buffalo.
5. My _____ job today is to cut the grass.
6. My horse's _____ is beautiful.
7. I paid a large _____ of money for my radio.
8. I would love _____ grapes.
9. I _____ him a present.
10. Carlos bought a nine-_____ postcard.
11. There are _____ quarters in two dollars.
12. I can't remember what I _____ for lunch.
13. Don't _____ your money.
14. Put the belt around your _____.
15. Please _____ for me.
16. I want to check my _____ on the scale.
17. See you next _____.
18. I'm too _____ to get out of bed.
19. I bought some pottery _____ at the fair.
20. I am going to _____ my new coat today.

What's the Big Idea?

Homophones are pronounced the same but have different meanings and usually different spellings. The meaning tells you which spelling to use.

Proofreading

Titles of books, magazines, and newspapers are underlined in a paragraph or story. Read the following article. Write and underline six titles. Find four list words that are misspelled. Write them correctly.

The Daily Times is running a series of articles on diets this weak. Yesterday, they reviewed two new books entitled Waist Your Waist Away and Don't Wait to Lose Weight.

Tomorrow they are reviewing sum magazines on dieting, such as Waist Control, Wait and You, and Calories and Exercise.

Handwriting

_____ *k* *h* _____ The letters **k** and **h** have tall loops. Make sure the loops are not too big or too small. Write the words *weak* and *weight*, paying careful attention to the **k** and **h**.

SPELLBOUND

Fill in each blank below with a list word to form an open or closed compound. Write the compound words. The first one is done for you.

a. someday
b. ____thing
c. ____how
d. silver____
e. hard____
f. glass____
g. ironing ____
h. shuffle____
i. clip____
j. ____end
k. ____day
l. ____night

Choose the list or lists of words you want to learn.
Then complete the activities next to each list you choose.

Use review words to complete the sentences.
1. We have __(a)__ tickets __(b)__ the carnival. Mary has one.
2. Let's use __(a)__ tickets today, and maybe Mary can go __(b)__ .

Review Words

too
to
two
our

---

1. Write the word that fits each spelling pattern.
   day __(a)__   sleigh __(b)__

2. Complete the sentence.
   He __(a)__ the ball __(b)__ the window.

Big Idea Words

through
threw
way
weigh

Unscramble the letters to match the definitions.
1. the same size and shape   (neungtocr)
2. the relation of the circumference of a circle to its diameter, or 3.14   (ip)
3. *scribe* means "write" and *circum* means "around"; draw a line around   (crcumiscerib)
4. *equi* means "equal" and *lateral* means "at the side"; having all sides equal   (aeelqurliat)

Content Words

pi
equilateral
congruent
circumscribe

Study Hint!

With homophones, the meaning tells which particular word to use in writing. Think of a way to associate each homophone with its meaning or correct usage.

WORDS ENDING IN ion

Part A

Say the words in the list below. Write the words.

1. selection
2. rejection
3. intersection
4. subtraction
5. detection
6. complication
7. violation
8. duplication
9. termination
10. television
11. persuasion
12. subdivision
13. collision
14. compression
15. confession
16. impression
17. depression
18. expression
19. fiction *
20. champion *

Many English nouns are formed by adding *-ion* to verbs. Sometimes there are spelling changes.

● Write the list words formed from these base words:

select   complicate
televise   compress

✳Wild Words   *Fiction* came into English from Latin as a noun. It was not formed from an English word.

In the word *champion*, **ion** is not a suffix. *Champ* is a shortened form of *champion*, not its base word.

Test Score: _____ —20   **88**   *Part A Score:* _____ —4

Part B

1. Write the list word formed from each base word.

televise	persuade	subdivide
collide	select	reject
intersect	subtract	detect
compress	confess	impress
depress	express	

2. Write the two wild words.

3. Write the list word that is the noun form of each underlined word below.

   a. Having two jobs caused a <u>complicate</u> for Jan.

   b. Speeding is a <u>violate</u> of the law.

   c. The soccer game is on <u>televise</u> tonight.

   d. Her answer was a <u>duplicate</u> of mine.

   e. It took a lot of <u>persuade</u> to make him go.

   f. The <u>terminate</u> of my contract is tomorrow.

   g. The new <u>subdivide</u> will be finished soon.

   h. The train <u>collide</u> was very serious.

What's the Big Idea?

When *-ion* is added to a verb, the word becomes a noun.
Many times there are spelling changes when *-ion* is added.

Dictionary

pro fes sion al (prə-fesh′ə nəl), **1** of or having to do with a profession; appropriate to a profession: *Our doctor has a professional seriousness unlike his ordinary joking manner.* **2** engaged in a profession: *A lawyer or a doctor is a professional person.* **3** making a business or trade of something which others do for pleasure: *a professional ballplayer, professional musicians.* **4** person who does this. **5** undertaken or engaged in by professionals rather than amateurs: *a professional ball game.* 1-3,5 *adj.,* 4 *n.* —**pro fes′sion al ly,** *adv.*

Not all forms of a word are listed in a dictionary as entry words. For example, if you wanted to check the meaning or spelling of *professionally,* you would look up *professional.* Words like *professionally, televised,* or *duplicating* are run-on entries. Look at the entry at the left and notice that *professionally* comes at the end of the entry.

Write the word you would look up in a dictionary in order to find each run-on entry below.

1. violating
2. collided
3. commercially
4. complicating
5. fictionally
6. persuaded
7. terminating
8. selectively
9. duplicated
10. tentatively

SPELLBOUND

Spelling words correctly is important for police officers who make out accident reports. Pretend you are a police officer and write an accident report using the list words *intersection, collision,* and *violation.*

Part D

Choose the list or lists of words you want to learn.
Then complete the activities next to each list you choose.

---

1. Write the word that has the same final syllable as *mission*.

2. Write the three words that have the same final syllable as *action*.

3. Write a list word in the pattern of *caution*.

Big Idea Words

caution

aggression

vocation

option

Use the glossary or a dictionary to write the challenge word that means:
1. get into or through
2. spread in different directions
3. take in or suck up
4. use up

Challenge Words

absorb

consume

dissipate

penetrate

Use your glossary, if necessary, to help you answer the questions and complete the sentences.
1. Most adjectives have comparative and superlative forms with *-er* and *-est* endings. Which is which?   -er   -est
2. Sentences are made up of subjects and predicates. In the sentence "I like big cats," *I* is the subject and *like big cats* is the ____. The word *big* is a ____ of cats.

Content Words

modifier

predicate

comparative

superlative

Study Hint!

In many words ending in **ion**, the **ion** is preceded by **s**, **ss**, or **t**. Group your words by their endings.

VERB INFLECTIONS

Part A

Say the words in the list below. Write the words.

1. *comes*
2. *chases*
3. *receives*
4. *begins*
5. *hired*
6. *appreciated*
7. *having*
8. *hoping*
9. *whipped*
10. *worshipped*
11. *tugging*
12. *slipping*
13. *studies*
14. *dries*
15. *worried*
16. *carried*
17. *hurrying*
18. *mystifying*
19. *bitten* *
20. *paid* *

In words 5–16, there was a change in the base word when the ending *-ed, -ing,* or *-es* was added. Write the numbers of the words that illustrate the changes below.

- A final **e** was dropped in words ____.
- A final consonant was doubled in words ____.
- A final **y** was changed to **i** in words ____.
- Underline the verb endings with no spelling change.

✱Wild Words   When *-en* is added to *bite* to form *bitten,* the final **e** is dropped and the **t** is doubled.

Paid is formed from *pay.* It rhymes with the word *maid.*

Part B

1. Write the form of the underlined word that correctly completes each unfinished sentence.
    a. I usually <u>come</u> to parties late, but Carlos ＿＿ early.
    b. My dog won't <u>chase</u> cats, but he ＿＿ cows.
    c. Mr. Ching ＿＿ four women and will <u>hire</u> more.
    d. Rose has to <u>study</u> hard, but her sister never ＿＿.
    e. We <u>receive</u> our mail early; Jim ＿＿ his late.
    f. Are you ＿＿ for money, or do you <u>hope</u> for fame?
    g. Jo ＿＿ part of the bill and will <u>pay</u> the rest.
    h. Big items <u>dry</u> slowly, but a small item ＿＿ quickly.
    i. I <u>begin</u> my homework early, but my sister ＿＿ late.
    j. I didn't think my pup would <u>bite</u>, but I was ＿＿.
    k. The puzzle didn't <u>mystify</u> me, but it is ＿＿ Ted.

2. Write the list words that complete the chart below.

	-ing	*-ed*
a. appreciate	appreciating	＿＿
b. tug	＿＿	tugged
c. worship	worshipping	＿＿
d. slip	＿＿	slipped
e. hurry	＿＿	hurried
f. carry	carrying	＿＿
g. worry	worrying	＿＿
h. whip	whipping	＿＿
i. have	＿＿	had

What's the Big Idea?

When the endings *-es, -ed,* or *-ing* are added to verbs, a final consonant may be doubled, a final **e** may be dropped, or a final **y** may be changed to an **i**.

Proofreading

Quotation marks (" ") are used around a direct quotation, or the exact words spoken by a person: *The coach said, "I'm happy."*

Don't use quotation marks around sentences like: *The coach said that she was happy.*

Read the article below. Copy the first and last words of the coach's statements and put quotation marks before and after them. Write the four misspelled words.

Coach Jill Goldman admitted today that she was werried before the championship game. We're a young team, and I didn't really believe we would win the state championship, she said.

During an interview after Lane High whiped Jefferson, Ms. Goldman stated, I told the players to do their best. They did, and I appreshiated their efforts.

As she was herrying to her team, Coach Goldman called, This has to be the happiest day of my life.

SPELLBOUND

Study the form of the poem below, which is a cinquain.

Line 1: one word — sleet
Line 2: two words — icy wet
Line 3: three words ending in **ing** — slipping, sliding, spinning
Line 4: four words — Cars driving on ice
Line 5: one word similar in meaning to line 1 — storm

Try writing your own cinquain to share with your classmates. See whether you can use *-ing* forms of list words.

Part D

Choose the list or lists of words you want to learn.
Then complete the activities next to each list you choose.

---

1. Write review words that are forms of:
   a. stop   b. forget
   c. excite   d. write
2. Write the words in which **e** is dropped when *-ing* is added to a base word.

Review Words

exciting
writing
stopped
forgetting

Write the words that are forms of:
1. rely   2. control
3. force   4. announce

Big Idea Words

controlling
forcing
relied
announced

Write the word for each clue.

1. sea northeast of Central America
2. island in the Caribbean Sea
3. peninsula in Mexico and Central America
4. mountains in eastern United States

Content Words

Jamaica
Yucatan
  Peninsula
Caribbean
Appalachian
  Mountains

Study Hint!

Write your list words as someone dictates them. Check your words and note how any misspelled ones differ from the correct spellings. Write misspelled words correctly.

REVIEW

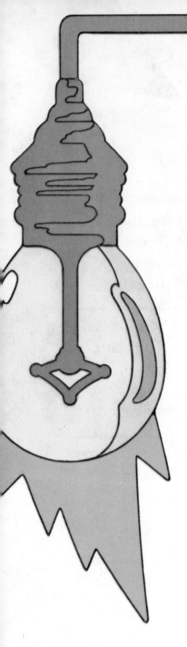

Here are some steps to help you study your words.

Before you write each word:
Look at the word.
Look at the letters.
Say the word.
Listen to the sounds.
When you write each word:
Copy the word from your list.
Write the word without looking at it.
After you write each word:
Check the word with your list.
Did you make a mistake?
Notice where you made the mistake and begin
the steps again.

Write the five review words for each lesson. Did you remember to record your misspelled or most troublesome words after the lesson test? If you forgot, write any you think of now under the heading Personal Words.

Lesson 19: Words with Latin Prefixes

Review Words	Personal Words
1. comfortable	1. _____
2. committee	2. _____
3. cooperate	3. _____
4. condominium✱	4. _____
5. coalition✱	5. _____

Lesson 20: More Words with Latin Prefixes

Review Words	Personal Words
1. declaration	1. _____
2. develop	2. _____
3. disguised	3. _____
4. surprise*	4. _____
5. surrounded*	5. _____

Lesson 21: Homophones

Review Words	Personal Words
1. sent	1. _____
2. waist	2. _____
3. week	3. _____
4. ware*	4. _____
5. wear*	5. _____

Lesson 22: Words Ending in ion

Review Words	Personal Words
1. detection	1. _____
2. termination	2. _____
3. collision	3. _____
4. fiction*	4. _____
5. champion*	5. _____

Lesson 23: Verb Inflections

Review Words	Personal Words
1. hoping	1. _____
2. dries	2. _____
3. hurrying	3. _____
4. bitten*	4. _____
5. paid*	5. _____

1. Write the six words that each contain one set of double letters.

2. Write the word that has three sets of double letters.

3. Write the words that mean the same thing or almost the same thing as the following words or phrases.

   a. work together
   b. proclamation
   c. astonish

   d. a kind of dwelling
   e. dressed to look like someone else
   f. closed in on all sides

   g. alliance
   h. grow
   i. at ease

   j. winner
   k. a crash
   l. moving quickly

4. Write a homophone for each word below.

   a. waste
   b. cent

   c. weak
   d. ware

5. Write four words that end with /shən/.

6. Write the words that have these roots.

   a. hope
   b. dry
   c. pay

7. Write the word that can be added to each of these words to make compound words.

   earthen   silver   tin   glass

8. In the lines below there are eighteen words. Find and write each word correctly.

surprisehurryingbitten

disguiseddevelopcommittee

hopingpaidcondominium

cooperatedetectionsurrounded

warefictiontermination

comfortablewearwaist

Test Yourself
Find the misspelled word in each group. Then write it correctly.

1. a. coalition   b. coperate
   c. committee   d. comfortable

2. a. disguised   b. surrounded
   c. surprise   d. develope

3. a. wast   b. week
   c. scent   d. ware

4. a. collision   b. champion
   c. detetion   d. fiction

5. a. dries   b. hopping
   c. paid   d. bitten

Personal Words
Choose five of your personal words that gave you the most difficulty and write them in alphabetical order.

Write at least three of your personal words together like the examples above. See if a friend can separate and write the words correctly.

99

MORE WORDS WITH PREFIXES

Part A

Say the words in the list below. Write the words.

1. *invent*
2. *including*
3. *instead*
4. *entrance*
5. *enclose*
6. *embroidery*
7. *employ*
8. *improve*
9. *immediately*
10. *excellent*
11. *excitement*
12. *expert*
13. *enormous*
14. *event*
15. *transcontinental*
16. *transparent*
17. *transport*
18. *tradition*
19. *traffic**
20. *environment**

Each word in the list contains a prefix. Most of these prefixes were already parts of the words when they came into English from other languages. Write the numbers of the words that begin with the following prefixes.

- *in-*, also spelled *en-*, *em-*, or *im-*
- *ex-* or its shorter form *e-*
- *trans-* or *tra-*

*Wild Words   A "break in *traffic*" comes between the two **f**'s. Don't mess up the *environment*; there's an **o** in it.

1. Say each list word carefully, stressing the first syllable. Then write it under the letters that spell the first syllable. Hint! (i nôr′məs) doesn't belong under **en**, but it doesn't belong under **in** either.

in	en	ex
im	em	e
trans	tra	

2. Write the list words for these meanings.

   a. very large
   b. carry across
   c. right now
   d. get better
   e. very good or fine
   f. a happening
   g. custom or pattern
   h. easily seen through

EXCELLENT

What's the Big Idea?

The best way to remember whether a word begins with -in, en-, em-, im-; with ex- or e-; or with trans- or tra- is to make sure you pronounce it correctly.

Part C
Dictionary

Some words have more than one spelling. Because words are listed in a dictionary in alphabetical order, the different spellings of the same word are in different places in the dictionary. Look up the entry *thru* in the glossary. Notice that the meaning of the word is not given there. Since *through* is the more common spelling, the meaning will be found under that entry. Look it up.

Use the glossary to find the more common spelling for each word below. Write that spelling.

1. inclose	2. intrust	3. sirup
4. tho	5. good-bye	6. racquet

SPELLBOUND

Write the list words that could be substituted for the underlined words and phrases in the paragraph below. Use the glossary, if necessary.

    Persons in the control tower at a busy airfield direct the (1) <u>coming and going</u> of both intercontinental and (2) <u>cross-continent</u> flights. Pilots of planes that (3) <u>carry</u> people or freight depend on the directions of an (4) <u>unusually skillful person</u> in the control tower for safe landings and takeoffs. Airfield managers (5) <u>hire</u> persons who have (6) <u>very good</u> powers of concentration and who can use complicated equipment for air traffic control.

Write a paragraph, describing a career in which you are interested.

Choose the list or lists of words you want to learn.
Then complete the activities next to each list you choose.

Write the review words that follow the spelling patterns
below for the past tense.

1. thought   2. paid   3. talked   4. tagged

Review Words

grabbed
bought
frightened
laid

Write the word that goes with each clue.
1. to change from one to another
2. to enter with force
3. to fill with enthusiasm
4. the opposite of *emigrant;* one who enters a country

Big Idea Words

transfer
invade
enthuse
✗immigrant

---

1. Use the meanings of the Greek words below to match
   the descriptions and names of dinosaurs.

deinos—terrible   *saurus*—lizard   *brachion*—arm
bronto—thunder   *tyrannus*—tyrant   *nodos*—toothless

a. Its walk sounded like thunder.
b. Its front legs were like arms.
c. It had no teeth.
d. It was a ruthless king of dinosaurs.
2. Make a chart comparing the dinosaurs above.

Challenge Words

tyrannosaurus
nodosaurus
brachiosaurus
brontosaurus

Study Hint!

Group words with common first or last syllables.
Concentrate on spelling correctly the parts they have in
common, and you will become a better speller.

THE CONSONANT SOUNDS
/g/, /gz/, /j/, AND /gw/

Part A

Say the words in the list below. Write the words.

1. guard
2. guide
3. guitar
4. league
5. fatigue
6. synagogue
7. example
8. exact
9. exhaust
10. dungeon
11. pigeon
12. sergeant
13. contagious
14. region
15. religion
16. language
17. penguin
18. jaguar
19. tongue *
20. margarine *

Some consonant spelling patterns occur rarely.

● Write the first word for each sound and spelling clue.

/g/ spelled **gu**   /g/ spelled **gue**   /gz/ spelled **x**

/j/ spelled **gi**   /j/ spelled **g** before **e**   /gw/ spelled **gu**

● Underline the letters that spell /g/ in the list words.

*Wild Words   The sound /j/ is usually spelled **j** before **a**, but in *margarine* it is spelled **g** before **a**. The consonant sound /ng/ is usually spelled **ng**, but in *tongue* it is **ngue**.

Part B

1. When **g** comes before an **e** or an **i**, it usually has the sound /j/. Write the six list words in which **gi** or **g** before **e** stands for /j/.

2. Write the words that contain these sounds and spelling patterns.

   /g/ spelled **gu**
   /g/ spelled **gue**
   /gz/ spelled **x** or **xh**
   /gw/ spelled **gu**

3. Write a list word that goes with each pair of words given below.

   a. banjo, ukulele
   b. private, captain
   c. prison, cave
   d. lead, direct
   e. church, temple
   f. mouth, teeth
   g. butter, sour cream

What's the Big Idea?

The sound /g/ is sometimes spelled **gu** or **gue**; /gz/ is spelled **x** or **xh**; /j/ can be spelled **gi** or **g** before **e**; and in a few words /gw/ is spelled **gu**.

Part C
Dictionary

mar gar ine
(mär′jər ən *or*
mär′jə rēn′)

re cord (ri kôrd′ *for 1;*
rek′ərd *for 2*), **1** set
down in writing to keep
for future use. **2** a thin,
flat disk used on a
phonograph. 1 *v.*, 2 *n.*

Occasionally a dictionary entry has more than one
pronunciation. Both pronunciations shown for *margarine* are
correct whenever the word is used.

In a word like *record,* however, the correct pronunciation
depends upon the meaning of the word in context. The
entry shows which pronunciation is used for each definition.

1. Say each pair of pronunciations below. Then write the
   word for which they stand.
   a. (krēk *or* krik)   b. (bə lō′nē *or* be lō′nə)
   c. (en′və lōp *or* än′və lōp)
2. Which pronunciation of *record* would you use as you
   read aloud the sentence below?
   Kim scratched her new stereo *record.*

Handwriting

The letters **j** and **p** extend below the base line. Pay special
attention to the **j** and **p** as you write the words *penguin* and
jaguar.

SPELLBOUND

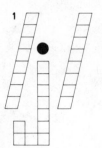

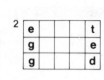

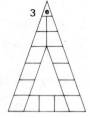

Use list words to complete
each puzzle.
1. three words with /j/
2. three words that begin
   and end with the letters
   given
3. three words with /gz/

Choose the list or lists of words you want to learn.
Then complete the activities next to each list you choose.

Use review words to complete the sentences.

1. There are 365 days, 52 weeks, and 12 _____ in a year.
2. The second month is _____.
3. _____ and Sunday are weekend days.
4. The _____ pages of Rick's calendar got lost.

Review Words
February
months
Saturday
loose

---

1. Write the words that are the opposite of:
   entrance, gal, innocence

2. Write the word with /j/ spelled **g** before **e**.

3. Write a list word with the same spelling pattern as
   surgeon.

Big Idea Words
guilt
surgeon
guy
exit

Use content words to complete the paragraph.

Linda does (1) , or practice exercises, before she enters
a gymnastic contest. These help her to (2) up. She is sure
she will be (3) many points because she feels very (4)
today and knows she can move quickly.

Content Words
agile
limber
warm-ups
scoring

Study Hint!

When studying a list word, pay particular attention to
any unusual spelling patterns in it. Cover the word,
write it, and then check your spelling.

REGULAR AND IRREGULAR PLURALS

Part A

Say the words in the list below. Write the words.

1. *ladies*
2. *women*
3. *gentlemen*
4. *people*
5. *themselves*
6. *mice*
7. *cattle*
8. *fowl*
9. *hose*
10. *riches*
11. *bacteria*
12. *trivia*
13. *ravioli*
14. *crises*
15. *oases*
16. *scarves*
17. *thieves*
18. *headquarters*
19. *graffiti* *
20. *UFO's* *

The list words are plural forms. Some are irregular plurals and others, like *cattle,* have no singular form.

● Write the first list word that follows each pattern.
thief, thieves   oasis, oases
trivium, trivia

*Wild Words   *Graffiti* are drawings or writings on walls. You seldom see one graffito by itself.

The plural for *UFO* is formed like the plurals for letters and numbers are formed. You add **'s** to this abbreviation.

1. Change **is** to **es** to form the plurals of *oasis* and *crisis.*

2. Change the final **o** to **i** to form the plurals of the words *graffito* and *raviolo.*

3. Change **um** to **a** to form the plurals of the Latin words *bacterium* and *trivium.*

4. Change **f** to **v** and add **es** to form the plurals of *scarf* and *thief.*

5. Write the list words that are the plural forms of the underlined words.

   a. The <u>lady</u> <u>herself</u> saw the <u>UFO</u>.
   b. The <u>gentleman</u> watched the <u>woman</u> catch the <u>mouse</u>.

6. Read the definitions below. Then write the words that can stand for the singular and plural.

   a. the main office   b. a bird or group   c. clothing for the feet
                      of birds   and/or legs

7. Write a list word to go with each word below. These list words are always in the plural form.
   a. persons   b. cows   c. wealth

What's the Big Idea?

Some words have irregular plurals. Other words, such as *cattle* and *people,* are always plural in normal use. Different languages form plurals in different ways.

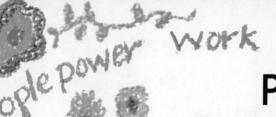

Proofreading

Exclamation marks are used to emphasize an idea or to show strong feelings. The exclamation mark is placed before the end quotation marks if it is part of a quoted remark.

Add two exclamation marks in the paragraphs below. Write three misspelled words correctly.

"My street used to be nice. Now look at all this garbage and filth" Mrs. Jones complained.

"My street is the same" said Mrs. Cirilo. "Let's get the peple to clean up the filth and plant flowers."

Later, the two laidies said proudly,, "People can really change things themselfs"

SPELLBOUND

Look at the graffiti in the picture. Work with your classmates in creating a graffiti board. Write slogans, humorous statements, short rhymes, or interesting bits of trivia for the board. Try to use words from recent spelling lists in each graffito.

Part D

Choose the list or lists of words you want to learn.
Then complete the activities next to each list you choose.

Write the review word that belongs with each group.

1. seconds, ____, hours
2. never, ____, always
3. buddies, pals, ____
4. poles, boots, ____

Review Words

friends

minutes

skis

sometimes

Use the glossary to match
exact meanings and
challenge words. Write
the words in the puzzle.

1. a reminder
2. a keepsake
3. having tender feelings
4. a longing for things
   far away or past

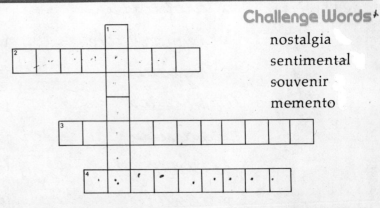

Challenge Words

nostalgia

sentimental

souvenir

memento

Write the words that match the clues. Use the glossary or
a dictionary.

1. the smallest known agent that causes diseases
2. two diseases caused by viruses
3. a drug that fights bacteria but not viruses

Content Words

virus

measles

antibiotic

bronchitis

Study Hint!

Reviewing the things you learned about irregular plurals
in Part B of this lesson will help you remember how to
spell the list words.

WORDS ENDING WITH /ə bəl/ AND /əns/

Part A

Say the words in the list below. Write the words.

1. durable
2. lovable
3. profitable
4. remarkable
5. vegetable
6. horrible
7. possible
8. responsible
9. terrible
10. convertible

11. balance
12. distance
13. endurance
14. performance
15. absence
16. experience
17. independence
18. sentence
19. ambulance *
20. occurrence *

The words in the list end with **able** or **ible** and with **ance** or **ence**. The spellings **able** and **ible** stand for the sounds /ə bəl/ and **ance** and **ence** stand for /əns/.

● Write the first list words that end with **able** and **ible**.
● Write the first list words that end with **ance** and **ence**.
● Underline the letters that spell /ə bel/ in words 1–10.

＊Wild Words   The word *ambulance* comes from French words that mean "a walking hospital."

To spell *occurrence* correctly, remember that there are two c's and two r's, and that /əns/ is spelled **ence**.

Part B

1. Write the five list words that end with **ance.**

2. Write the five list words that end with **ible.**

3. Write the five list words that end with **able.**

4. Write the five list words that end with **ence.**

5. Sometimes the spelling of the base word will show whether a related word is spelled with **ance** or **ence.** Write the list word related to: *distant, absent, independent.*

6. Write the two words related to *horror* and *terror.*

7. Use list words to complete the story.

   Odd things always seem to occur on my aunt's travels, but the strangest   (a)   of all was her disastrous   (b)   in a traffic accident. Aunt Em was   (c)   for a wreck between an   (d)   and a horse-drawn   (e)   cart. Her rented   (f)   wasn't even scratched.

What's the Big Idea?

Since either **able** or **ible** spells the sounds /ə bəl/ and since either **ance** or **ence** spells /əns/, it is necessary to memorize words containing these spellings.

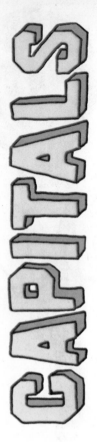

Part C
Proofreading

The names of people, specific places, things, and days must begin with capital letters: The King School gym team will be at the Howard Fieldhouse on Friday.

Find eight words that need capital letters in the announcement below and write the words correctly. Find two misspelled words and write them correctly.

The lincoln school band preformance will be at the silver stadium on thursday. The remarkible band will be directed by ms. beth brown.

Handwriting

The letters **l** and **e** are both looped. The **l** is a tall looped letter and the **e** is a short looped letter. Write the word *lovable* and pay special attention to the letters **l** and **e**.

SPELLBOUND

1. Proofread the sign at the left. Write the misspelled word correctly.
2. Use the words *possible, durable,* and *experience* to complete the want ads below.

a. New position
Paid strictly by your performance. It's
_____ to make a lot of money.
Write P. O. Box 86

b. Wanted
Responsible person to run profitable candy business. No _____ necessary.
Call 868-2121

c. For Sale
New _____ dishes.
Simply can't break.
Twenty dollars down.
Balance on terms.
Call 626-6132

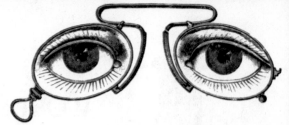

Part D

Choose the list or lists of words you want to learn.
Then complete the activities next to each list you choose.

---

1. Write a word that fits each group of related words.
   a. vision, ____, visibility
   b. audio, auditorium, ____
   c. allow, allowable, ____
   d. ____, probably, improbable

2. Write a list word in the pattern of *audience.*

Big Idea Words

probable
visible
allowance
audience

---

1. Write the three words that begin with the prefix *re-*.

2. Write the word that means "great anger or rage."

Challenge Words

wrath
rebuttal
rebuke
refute

Use the diagram to match the words and definitions.
1. a line through the center of a circle
2. the distance around a circle
3. a quarter of a circle
4. any part of a circumference

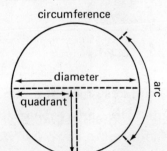

Content Words

circumference
diameter
quadrant
arc

Study Hint!

Make four columns on your paper with the headings
able, ible, ance, and **ence.** Write each list word
in the correct column.

WORDS ENDING WITH SUFFIXES

Part A

Say the words in the list below. Write the words.

1. relative
2. attractive
3. executive
4. creative
5. effective
6. legislative
7. detective
8. championship
9. hardship
10. leadership
11. relationship
12. ownership
13. penmanship
14. creature
15. architecture
16. legislature
17. furniture
18. departure
19. miniature*
20. temperature*

The suffixes *-ive*, *-ship*, and *-ure* are all used to make nouns. The suffix *-ive* is also used to make adjectives.

● Write the first two list words that end with *-ive*.
● Write the first two list words that end with *-ship*.
● Write the first two list words that end with *-ure*.

✻Wild Words   *Miniature* and *temperature* each have four syllables. Both words are often misspelled because people sometimes say them with only three syllables. Both words are easier to spell if pronounced with four syllables each: (min′ē ə chŭr) and (tem′pər ə chər).

Part B

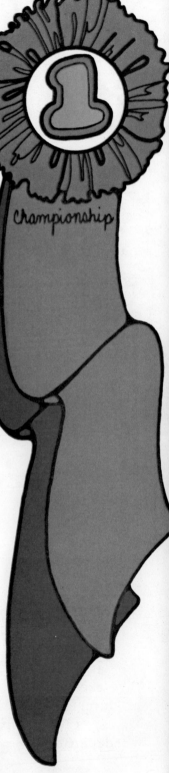

1. Write seven words that end with *-ure.* Notice that there is a **t** before the suffix and that the syllable is pronounced /chǝr/ in each word.

2. Write seven words that end with *-ive.*

3. Write six words that end with *-ship.*

4. Write two words that are related to each word below.

   a. create   b. legislate   c. relate

5. When dividing a word which has a suffix that begins with a consonant or a consonant blend, divide the word before that consonant or blend. Examples: *companion-ship; sportsman-ship.*

   Divide the following words before the final suffix.
   championship   ownership   penmanship

6. Use a list word to complete the sentence.
   The three branches of government are called the judicial, legislative, and ____ branches.

What's the Big Idea?
The suffixes *-ive, -ship,* and *-ure* are all used to make nouns. The suffix *-ive* is also used to make adjectives.

Part C

Dictionary

At the end of a line, most words with more than one syllable can be divided between syllables, with part of the word on one line, and part on the next line.

Study the different ways the word *architecture* is divided below. Then look up *detective* and *legislature* in the dictionary to see how they are divided.

ar chi tec ture

_____ ar-	_____ archi-	_____ architec-
chitecture _____	tecture _____	ture _____

Handwriting

_____ *N* *u* _____ The letters **v** and **u** look somewhat alike, but are different in two important ways. The **v** begins with an overhill stroke, and the **u** begins with an uphill stroke. Also, the **u** returns to the line before connecting with the next letter; the **v** does not.

Write the words *creature* and *creative.* Pay close attention to the letters **u** and **v.**

SPELLBOUND

attr*A*ctive
exe*C*utive
furni*T*ure
    *O*wnership
depa*R*ture

Here is a game you can play with your spelling words. Write a word down the page in capital letters. Then write a list word for each letter in the word you chose. Look at the finished game at the left. Then try the game with the word *minus.*

Part D

Choose the list or lists of words you want to learn.
Then complete the activities next to each list you choose.

---

1. Write the review word for each pronunciation.
   a. (kwīt)   b. (kwī′ət)
2. Write the review word that follows the same spelling
   pattern as each pair below.
   a. brief, thief, _____
   b. movie, collie, _____

Review Words

quiet
prairie
chief
quite

Write the word that ends with each suffix.
1. *-ative*   2. *-itive*
3. *-ure*   4. *-ship*

Big Idea Words

disclosure
sensitive
representative
sportsmanship

The Greek combining form *hydro-* means "water."
Unscramble the letters to match the words and definitions.
1. electricity from water power (hydrotcicrlee)
2. a plane that lands on water (hydronaelp)
3. a fin just below the water line that raises a boat out of
   water at high speeds (hydroloif)
4. having to do with the force or motion of liquids, such as
   water (hydromnaydci)

Challenge Words

hydrodynamic
hydroelectric
hydroplane
hydrofoil

Study Hint!

When you study words with several syllables, pronounce
each word carefully and spell each syllable.

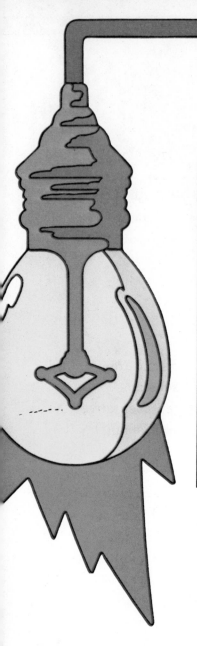

REVIEW

Here are some steps to help you study your words.

Before you write each word:
    Look at the word.
    Look at the letters.
    Say the word.
    Listen to the sounds.
When you write each word:
    Copy the word from your list.
    Write the word without looking at it.
After you write each word:
    Check the word with your list.
    Did you make a mistake?
    Notice where you made the mistake and begin
        the steps again.

Write the five review words for each lesson. Did you remember to record your misspelled or most troublesome words after the lesson test? If you forgot, write any you think of now under the heading Personal Words.

Lesson 25: More Words with Prefixes

Review Words	Personal Words
1. enclose	1. _____
2. immediately	2. _____
3. enormous	3. _____
4. traffic✳	4. _____
5. environment✳	5. _____

Lesson 26: The Consonant Sounds /g/, /gz/, /j/, and /gw/

Review Words	Personal Words
1. league	1. _____
2. exhaust	2. _____
3. sergeant	3. _____
4. tongue✻	4. _____
5. margarine✻	5. _____

Lesson 27: Regular and Irregular Plurals

Review Words	Personal Words
1. ladies	1. _____
2. people	2. _____
3. themselves	3. _____
4. graffiti✻	4. _____
5. UFO's✻	5. _____

Lesson 28: Words with /ə bəl/ and /əns/

Review Words	Personal Words
1. horrible	1. _____
2. terrible	2. _____
3. experience	3. _____
4. ambulance✻	4. _____
5. occurrence✻	5. _____

Lesson 29: Words Ending With Suffixes

Review Words	Personal Words
1. attractive	1. _____
2. penmanship	2. _____
3. creature	3. _____
4. miniature✻	4. _____
5. temperature✻	5. _____

1. Write the review word that rhymes with:
rose, Tahiti, active.

2. Write the words that end with:

ship	ible	ible
ance	ence	ence
ure	ure	ure

3. Write the review words that mean:
huge, at once, women, oleo.

4. Write the plural for the short form of *unidentified flying object.*

5. Write the words that mean:

   a. a police officer
   b. part of the mouth used for tasting
   c. autos coming and going along a road
   d. shut in on all sides
   e. use up
   f. association of sports clubs or teams

6. Read the paragraph below. Then use the pronunciation clues to write review words to complete the paragraph.

We got to talk to the major a. (lēg) baseball player. But instead of talking about baseball, he talked about how b. (pē′pəl) c. (eg zost′) natural resources by wasting them and how they ruin the d. (en vī′rən mənt) by littering. He said that people have only e. (ᴛʜem selvz′ *or* ᴛʜəm selvz′) to blame if they don't mend their ways.

a. ____, b. ____, c. ____,
d. ____, e. ____

7. The signs below show what happens when people get careless with their spelling. Find six misspelled words and write them correctly below.

CASITA ROSA
NEW HOURS 8 AM
12 NITE
MINATURE GOLF
OPEN

a

good food great drinks

LIVE INTERTAINM ENT FRI SAT

TER

EXCELLET MUSIC

FOOD DRINKS

b

Help Save peeps Lives

c

e-f

YOU CAN'T BEAT THE CAPT'NS DRUMSTICKS

d

Test Yourself

Find the misspelled word in each group of words below and write it correctly.

1. a. enclose   b. immediately
   c. traffic   d. environement

2. a. league   b. sargeant
   c. margarine   d. experience

3. a. themselves   b. graffiti
   c. ladys   d. people

4. a. horrible   b. occurrence
   c. experience   d. ambulence

5. a. attractive   b. creeture
   c. miniature   d. temperature

Personal Words

Make up some signs using personal words and leave out some troublesome letters. For example, *Showing Tonight* **Ter__ble Tessie and the Mini__ture Monster.** Trade signs with a friend and write each other's incomplete words correctly.

WORDS ENDING WITH
ent, ant, ate, AND age

Part A

Say the words in the list below. Write the words.

1. ancient
2. current
3. intelligent
4. patient
5. student
6. descendant
7. pleasant
8. servant
9. vacant
10. approximate

11. certificate
12. desperate
13. participate
14. separate
15. advantage
16. average
17. message
18. passage
19. messenger *
20. passenger *

The list words in this lesson end in **ent** or **ant,** pronounced /ənt/, or with **ate** or **age.** The spelling **age** is pronounced /ij/, and the pronunciation of **ate** varies according to whether **ate** is accented or not.

● Write the first two list words ending with:
ent, ant, ate, age.
● Underline **ent, ant, ate,** or **age** in each list word.

∗Wild Words   To spell *messenger* and *passenger,* the letters **age** in *message* and *passage* must be changed to **eng** before *-er* is added. Write the two wild words.

Part B

1. Write the five words that end with **ent**.

2. Write the five words that end with **ate**.

3. Write the four words that end with **ant**.

4. Write the four words that end with **age**.

5. Write the wild words.

Use the pronunciation clues to complete the sentences with list words.

The history 6. (stüd′nt) or (styüd′nt) went to the island to 7. (pär tis′ə pāt) in a study of 8. (ān′shənt) temples.
Fran needed to be 9. (in tel′ə jənt) and 10. (pā′shənt) in order to piece together the 11. (mes′ij) of the very old ruins.
She found a 12. (pas′ij) that led to a 13. (sep′ər it) temple and she was awarded a 14. (sər tif′ə kit) and fifty dollars.

What's the Big Idea?

The sounds /ənt/ are spelled **ent** or **ant**, and /ij/ is spelled **age**. The pronunciation of **ate** depends on whether the syllable is accented or unaccented.

Proofreading

Find four places where Mark forgot to put periods at the end of the sentences in his story. Write each word before the period and add the period.

Find four misspelled list words and write them correctly.

I'm a studnt of all kinds of desserts My currant favorite is coffee ice cream I like the plensent taste of the combination of sugar, cream, and coffee I must admit, however, that the aveage person my age usually likes chocolate better

 SPELLBOUND

1. Find at least three more list words to describe a person. Write the words.

   patient person   ____ person
   ____ person   ____ person

2. How many four- or five-letter words can you make from the letters in *descendant?* Eight words are good; twelve words are excellent. Write the words.

3. If you enjoyed the exercise above, do the same with one or more of the words that describe a person.

Part D

Choose the list or lists of words you want to learn. Then complete the activities next to each list you choose.

Use review words to complete the sentences.

1. Wishing and expecting to do well is ____.
2. A person who doesn't depend on others is ____.
3. A small copy of a car is a ____ car.
4. Something only you and a friend know is a ____.

Review Words

independent

hoping

secret

model

Use challenge words to complete the paragraph.

The club decided to have a __(1)__ to celebrate the first day of spring. Arnold wanted to have a __(2)__ and give prizes for the best costumes. Bea thought they should have a __(3)__ sale to make money for camp. Al insisted they should have a __(4)__ and sell candy, toys, and plants.

Challenge Words

1. festival
2. masquerade
3. rummage
4. bazaar

Use the pronunciation clues and the definitions to help you write the content words.

1. (dis′in fek′tənt), substance used to destroy germs
2. (im pyür′ə tē), whatever makes something unclean
3. (klôr′ə nāt), to treat with chlorine
4. (də lüt′) or (dī lüt′), to make weaker or thinner by adding liquid

Content Words

chlorinate

dilute

impurity

disinfectant

Study Hint!

When words end with the sounds /ənt/, check to make sure whether /ənt/ is spelled **ent** or **ant**. Study words ending in **ent**, **ant**, **ate**, and **age** in separate groups.

MULTISYLLABIC WORDS

Part A

Say the words in the list below. Write the words.

1. adventure
2. assignment
3. bicentennial
4. commandment
5. enjoyment
6. forgotten
7. permission
8. irregular
9. opponent
10. opposite
11. international
12. recital
13. refreshment
14. refrigerator
15. unpleasantness
16. department
17. uninhabited
18. untidiness
19. aeronautical *
20. synchronize *

The words in this lesson are each made up of a prefix, a root, and a suffix. Sometimes the prefixes and suffixes were already a part of the words when they came into English.

● Write the word that belongs in each group.
fresh, refresh   joy, enjoy

✳**Wild Words**   The root -chron- means "time." Have you ever heard someone say "*Synchronize* your watches"?

The first vowel sound in *aeronautical* is spelled **ae**.

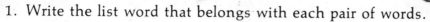

Part B

1. Write the list word that belongs with each pair of words.

vent, advent   sign, assign   joy, enjoy

pleasant, unpleasant nation, national fresh, refresh

cite, recite   tidy, untidy   part, depart

century, centennial   habit, inhabit   forget, forgot

2. Write the word that ends with the suffix *-ment* and means "a law."

3. Write the word that begins with the prefix *ir-* and means "not regular."

4. Write the two words that begin with the prefix *op-*.

5. Write the word that begins with the prefix *re-* and is a cold place to keep food.

6. Write the word that begins with the prefix *per-*.

7. Write the two wild words.

BICENTENNIAL

What's the Big Idea?

Some words have a root and both a prefix and a suffix. Sometimes the prefixes and suffixes were already a part of the words when they came into English.

Part C
Proofreading

dz., dozen or dozens.

E.S.T., Eastern Standard Time.

lb., pound. *pl.* **lb.** or **lbs.** [abbreviation of Latin *libra* pound]

R.I., Rhode Island.

U.S., the United States.

Abbreviations are letters that stand for words or phrases. Usually abbreviations are written with periods. Use the glossary samples at the left to help you write the correct abbreviations for the incorrect abbreviations in the sentences below.

1. *The grocery store ad read: 1 dz large eggs for 90¢ and 1 lb margarine for 40¢.*

2. *It is 9:00 E S T in New York right now.*

3. *Inez and her family moved to the U S this year.*

4. *We visited R I last summer.*

Handwriting

f h

Both the letters **f** and **h** are tall looped letters beginning with an uphill stroke. The letter **f** is also looped below the line. Write the word *refreshment* and pay special attention to the **f** and **h.**

SPELLBOUND

The Greek combining form **aero-** (sometimes spelled **a-e-r**) means "air," and occurs in many words other than *aeronautical.* Look up the words below in the dictionary, then use each in a sentence.

aerial   aerialist   aerosol   aeroplane   aerodynamic

Part D

Choose the list or lists of words you want to learn. Then complete the activities next to each list you choose.

---

1. Write the two words that rhyme with each other.

2. Supply the missing word in each quotation.

   a. "Little Jack Horner sat in a ____ . . . "
   b. "Oh ____ for spacious skies . . . "

Review Words
believe
corner
beautiful
receive

---

1. Write the words that contain these base words.

   a. agree   b. health   c. count   d. organize

2. Write the list word containing the base word *joy.*

Big Idea Words
unorganized
unhealthy
discounted
disagreeable

---

1. What did the *medic* call the *medicine?*

2. With what did the nurse *anoint* the burn?

3. Write a challenge word for each definition.
   a. a skin disease   b. an infection of the lungs

Challenge Words
pneumonia
medication
acne
ointment

Study Hint!

When a word has a prefix and a suffix added to it, look at the root word first. This will help you learn to spell it.

EASILY CONFUSED WORDS

Part A

Say the words in the list below. Write the words.

1. carton
2. cartoon
3. cornet
4. coronet
5. dairy
6. diary
7. pen
8. pin
9. personal
10. personnel
11. pour
12. poor
13. sure
14. shore
15. vanilla
16. manila
17. wandered
18. wondered
19. recipe *
20. receipt *

The spellings of the two words in each pair in the list are often confused because the words look and sound so much alike. Context will tell which word to use:
Which holds milk—a *carton* or a *cartoon?*
Pronounce each word carefully and memorize its spelling.

＊Wild Words   *Recipe* has three syllables. *Receipt* has two syllables. Don't forget the **ei** after **c** and the /t/ spelled **pt** in *receipt.*

● Write the two wild words.

Part B

1. Some words have to be pronounced very carefully. Complete the sentences with the words indicated by the pronunciations.

Let's __(a)__ the ribbon on the pig in that __(b)__.	(pin) (pen)
I __(c)__ where you had __(d)__ while I was waiting on the corner.	(wun′dərd) (won′dərd)
The soldier played his __(e)__ when the __(f)__ was placed on the prince's head.	(kôr′net) (kôr′ə net)
This is __(g)__ syrup to __(h)__ on the pancakes.	(pu̇r) (pôr)
I was __(i)__ we would go to the __(j)__ today.	(shu̇r) (shôr)
I wrote about our trip to the __(k)__ in my __(l)__.	(der′ē) (dī′ər ē)
My little brother can't pronounce __(m)__ so he calls the cookies __(n)__ cookies.	(və nil′ə) (mə nil′ə)
Mom got a __(o)__ letter from the __(p)__ department telling her to come to work.	(pėr′sə nəl) (pėr′ sə nel′)
We put the old toys in the __(q)__ while we watched the __(r)__ on TV.	(kärt′n) (kär tün′)

2. Both *recipe* and *receipt* come from a Latin word that means "to take back." Put each in a sentence below.

   Grandmother gave me her __(a)__ for taffy.

   The store gave me a __(b)__ when I paid the bill.

What's the Big Idea?

Words that have similar sounds or spellings may be confusing. It is important to associate the pronunciation and spelling of each word with its meaning.

Part B Score: ________ *—20*

Dictionary

adj. adjective
adv. adverb
conj. conjunction
interj. interjection
n. noun
prep. preposition
pron. pronoun
v. verb

The parts of speech that an entry word can be, such as noun, verb, and adjective, are often shown at the end of an entry. The numbers before the abbreviations refer to the numbers of the definitions. In some dictionaries a key is given to explain the abbreviations for the parts of speech used in the entry.

pin (pin), **1** badge with a pin or clasp to fasten it to the clothing: *She wore her class pin.* **2** fasten or attach firmly to or on; tack; fasten as if with pins. **1** *n.,* **2** *v.,* **pinned, pin ning.** ↑
          Parts of speech

Look at the entry for *pin.* What parts of speech is *pin?*

Write the part of speech *pin* is in each sentence below.
1. You should *pin* on a patch before you sew it.
2. The members wanted a club *pin* to wear.

calm (käm *or* kälm), **1** not excited; peaceful: *Although she was frightened, she answered with a calm voice.* **2** absence of excitement; peacefulness: *The activity of the game was followed by an unusual calm.* **3** make or become calm: *I rocked the cradle to calm the crying baby.* **1** *adj.,* **2** *n.,* **3** *v.*

Refer to the entry for *calm.* Write what part of speech *calm* is in each sentence below.
1. Marcia is always *calm;* she never gets excited.
2. The uproar was followed by a *calm.*
3. You can *calm* him if anyone can.

Handwriting

The letter **h** is a tall looped letter. The letters **n** and **m** begin with overhill strokes. Write the words *shore* and *manila.* Pay special attention to **h, m,** and **n.**

SPELLBOUND

Find three misspelled words and write them correctly.

I shore would like to go to the diary and get some manila ice cream.

Part D

Choose the list or lists of words you want to learn. Then complete the activities next to each list you choose.

Use review words to complete the sentences or phrases.
1. Poko is the name of ____ watchdog.
2. A word that refers to a place: *here, where,* ____
3. A word that has the same spelling pattern as *when*
4. A word that fits the pattern: *greater than, smaller* ____

Review Words

their
there
then
than

---

1. Use the glossary to complete the sentences.
   a. Did you ever visit the U.S. ____ in Washington?
   b. Put a ____ letter at the beginning of a sentence.
   c. The head of our school is the ____.
   d. Being honest is an important ____ to live by.
2. Write the pair of easily confused list words in which the initial consonants differ.

Big Idea Words

capital
Capitol
principle
principal

Unscramble the letters to match the definitions.
1. low, dark, rainy clouds   (bstonmirtaus)
2. very thin, high clouds   (usrcri)
3. round, piled up clouds flat at bottom   (lumuusc)
4. weather scientist   (tltmroeogsioe)

Content Words

cirrus
cumulus
nimbostratus
meteorologist

Study Hint!

As you study the two words in each pair, pronounce the words carefully, note their spellings, and think about their meanings.

NAMES OF PLACES

Part A

Say the words in the list below. Write the words.

1. Hawaii
2. Idaho
3. Louisiana
4. Nebraska
5. Nevada
6. New Jersey
7. North Dakota
8. Rhode Island
9. South Dakota
10. Wisconsin
11. Alberta
12. British Columbia
13. Manitoba
14. Newfoundland
15. Nova Scotia
16. Ontario
17. Quebec
18. Saskatchewan
19. District of Columbia *
20. Puerto Rico *

List words 1–18 name states of the United States and provinces of Canada.
- Write the first two words that name states.
- Write the first two words that name provinces.
- Write state and province names that are open compounds.

✳Wild Words   Washington, D.C., is not in any state. D.C. stands for *District of Columbia.*

Puerto Rico is a self-governing island that is under the protection of the United States.

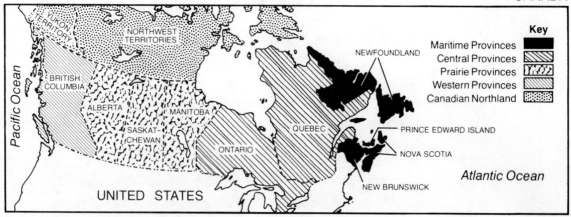

CANADA

Key
Maritime Provinces ▉
Central Provinces ▨
Prairie Provinces ▨
Western Provinces ▨
Canadian Northland ░

1. Use the map to find list words for each heading.
   a. Maritime Provinces (2)
   b. Central Provinces (2)
   c. Prairie Provinces (3)
   d. Western Province (1)

2. Write the place names that go with each clue.
   a. It was named after King Louis XIV of France.
   b. It is a group of islands in the Pacific Ocean.
   c. Part of its name is the name of a football shirt.
   d. Part of its name is a homophone for *road*.
   e. Its first three letters spell a woman's name.
   f. The Indian name for its chief river is *nebrathka*.
   g. Part of the Sierra Nevada Mountains are in it.
   h. It's named for *wishkinsing*, "place of beavers."
   i. Two states are named for the Dakota Indians.
   j. Two places are not states or provinces.

What's the Big Idea?

Proper names of places, such as states, provinces, cities, and islands, begin with capital letters.

Proofreading

Names of places begin with capital letters. Examples are Montreal, Quebec; Europe; Prince Edward Island.

Find four places where capital letters are needed, and four otherwise misspelled words. Write your corrections on a piece of paper.

> Place names reveal much about the history of north america. Quibec City got its name from the Algonquian Indian word <u>kebec</u>, which means "place where the river narrows." A winding river flows through the Sascatchuwon province. The Cree Indians called it <u>kis-is-ska-tchen-wan</u>, which means "river that turns around and runs."
>
> Nova Skotia means "New-scotland." Puerto rica means "rich port" in Spanish.

 # SPELLBOUND

The clues below explain the origin of place names. Write the list word or words that go with each clue.

1. *Nevado* is a Spanish word that means "snow clad."
2. Many places in the Americas are named for Columbus. Name two.
3. A British princess was named Louise Caroline Alberta.
4. Algonquian Indians called a narrow body of water *Manito waba*, which means "great spirit's strait."
5. An island that is part of England is named Jersey.

Choose the list or lists of words you want to learn. Then
complete the activities next to each list you choose.

---

1. Match the names of states and their abbreviations.
   a. Penn. or PA
   b. Okla. or OK
   c. Mass. or MA
   d. Conn. or CT
2. Write list words that match the abbreviations:
   a. Nev. or NV   b. La. or LA

Big Idea Words

Massachusetts
Pennsylvania
Connecticut
Oklahoma

Write each word that is given in pronunciation symbols.
1. The Jewish nation is called (iz′rē əl).
2. More soap is made in (sin′sə nat′ē) than any other city.
3. Lots of steel is produced in (pits′bèrg′).
4. Europe, Asia, and Africa are on the (med′ə tə rā′nē ən).

Challenge Words

Pittsburgh
Mediterranean
Israel
Cincinnati

Use *Greece, Pantheon,* and *Parthenon* in the first sentence.
Then write the word that completes the second sentence.
1. The (a) and the (b) are famous temples in (c) .
2. Both temples are examples of ancient Greek (d) .

Content Words

a. Pantheon
b. Parthenon
c. Greece
d. architecture

Study Hint!

Write the list words as someone dictates them. Check the
words and use the study steps to practice any you
misspelled.

ABBREVIATIONS AND ACRONYMS

Part A

Say the words in the list below. Write the abbreviations.

1. *a.m.*
2. *p.m.*
3. *Dr.*
4. *Mrs.*
5. *Mr.*
6. *Ms.*
7. *Jr.*
8. *U.S.A.*
9. *Co.*
10. *St.*
11. *Ave.*
12. *lbs.*
13. *no.*
14. *yrs.*
15. *radar*
16. *scuba*
17. *TV*
18. *NASA*
19. *flu*
20. *phone* ✳

Abbreviations, acronyms, and clipped forms are all shortened versions of words or phrases. Words are abbreviated by using certain letters. Acronyms are formed with the first letters from several words. Clipping replaces the word with a syllable.

● Write the abbreviations for:

County   Street   number   years

✳Wild Words   *Flu* and *phone* are both clipped forms of longer words. Don't confuse *flu*, which is short for *influenza*, with *flew*, the past tense of *fly*.

Part B

1. Study these Latin terms: *Meridiem* = noon; *Ante* = before; *Post* = after; *libra* = pound. Write abbreviations for *before noon, after noon,* and *pounds.*

2. Write the five abbreviations you might use as part of a person's name.

3. Some abbreviations can stand for more than one word. Write the two list words that can represent:
   a. company or county   b. Saint or street

4. Write abbreviations for:
   a. number   b. Avenue   c. years
   d. television   e. United States of America

5. Write the wild words.

6. An acronym is a word formed from the beginning letter or letters of a group of words or a term. For example: NOW = *N*ational *O*rganization for *W*omen.
   Write acronyms for:
   a. *s*elf-*c*ontained *u*nderwater *b*reathing *a*pparatus
   b. *N*ational *A*eronautics and *S*pace Administration
   c. *ra*dio *d*etecting *a*nd *r*anging

What's the Big Idea?

Many words can be abbreviated by using certain letters from that word. Most abbreviations are followed by periods. Some abbreviations form words called acronyms.

Dictionary

Dr. or **Dr**, Doctor.
Dr., **1** debtor. **2** Drive.

Abbreviations are listed as entry words in the dictionary. As you can see from the entry on the left, the definition is not always given for abbreviations.

1. Find the abbreviations below in your glossary. Then write the word or meaning that is listed for each abbreviation.

   a. op. cit.   b. loc. cit.   c. kl.
   d. cm.   e. ml.   f. dkg.

2. Write the words and their abbreviations below in alphabetical order. Abbreviations are alphabetized the same way all other words are alphabetized.

   Dr., doctor, number, no., pounds, lbs., Jr., junior

 SPELLBOUND

Below are some acronyms that are frequently used. Match them with their full names.

HUD   NATO   PAL   PUSH

North Atlantic Treaty Organization
People United to Save Humanity
Housing and Urban Development
Police Athletic League

Now try to make up some acronyms of your own, like: Parents for Improving Education—PIE.

Choose the list or lists of words you want to learn. Then
complete the activities next to each list you choose.

Write the word that best fits each clue below.

1. a December holiday   2. past tense of *hear*

3. persons   4. stimulation

Review Words
people
Christmas
heard
excitement

Many dates are listed as before or after Christ. *Anno
Domini* is "in the year of the Lord" in Latin.
1. Write the abbreviation or acronym for:
   a. 736 Before Christ   b. *Anno Domini* 1978
   c. North Atlantic Treaty Organization
   d. United Nations International Children's Emergency
      Fund
2. Write the list word that is the abbreviation for:
   a. company   b. television

Big Idea Words
A.D.
B.C.
UNICEF
NATO

Use the glossary to supply the missing challenge words.

1. If we don't __(a)__ the dam with more concrete, the water
   will __(b)__ it.
2. The captain was __(a)__ in his argument that hot __(b)__ of
   the pirates would cause them to surrender.

Challenge Words
persuasive
pursuit
reinforce
overwhelm

Study Hint!

Compare abbreviations and acronyms with their complete
versions. Focus on which letters have been kept in the
short version.

REVIEW

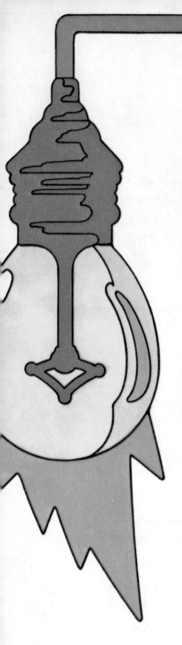

Here are some steps to help you study your words.

Before you write each word:
    Look at the word.
    Look at the letters.
    Say the word.
    Listen to the sounds.
When you write each word:
    Copy the word from your list.
    Write the word without looking at it.
After you write each word:
    Check the word with your list.
    Did you make a mistake?
    Notice where you made the mistake and begin
      the steps again.

Write the five review words for each lesson. Did you remember to record your misspelled or most troublesome words after each lesson test? If you forgot, write any you think of now under the heading Personal Words.

Lesson 31: Words Ending in ent, ant, ate, and age

Review Words	Personal Words
1. intelligent	1. _____
2. pleasant	2. _____
3. approximate	3. _____
4. messenger✷	4. _____
5. passenger✷	5. _____

Lesson 32: Multisyllabic Words

Review Words	Personal Words
1. forgotten	1. _____
2. permission	2. _____
3. irregular	3. _____
4. aeronautical*	4. _____
5. synchronize*	5. _____

Lesson 33: Easily Confused Words

Review Words	Personal Words
1. diary	1. _____
2. personnel	2. _____
3. vanilla	3. _____
4. recipe*	4. _____
5. receipt*	5. _____

Lesson 34: Names of Places

Review Words	Personal Words
1. Louisiana	1. _____
2. Rhode Island	2. _____
3. Wisconsin	3. _____
4. District of Columbia*	4. _____
5. Puerto Rico*	5. _____

Lesson 35: Abbreviations and Acronyms

Review Words	Personal Words
1. Dr.	1. _____
2. Mr.	2. _____
3. radar	3. _____
4. flu*	4. _____
5. phone*	5. _____

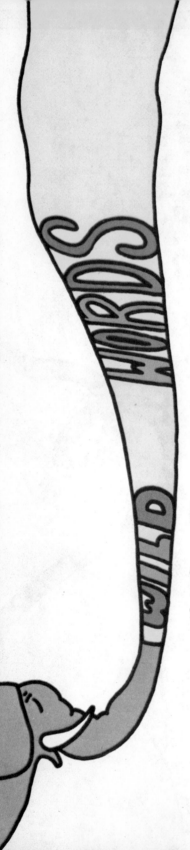

1. Use review words from Lesson 31 to complete the paragraph.

   The flight attendant was a. (in tel′ə jənt) and b. (plez′nt). His c. (ə prok′sə mit) height was six feet. The d. (pas′n jər) sitting next to me was a e. (mes′n jər) for the president.

2. Write the words in Lesson 32 that have the following roots: a. permit, b. regular, c. forget.

3. Write the two wild words from Lesson 32.

4. Use review words from Lesson 33 to complete the sentences.

   I like chocolate and a. (və nil′ə) ice cream.
   Dear b. (dī′ər ē), Today I met a new friend.
   May I have a c. (ri sēt′) for my payment?
   I have a marvelous d. (res′ə pē) for fudge.
   Can you direct me to the e. (per′sə nel′) office?

5. Write the names of the states in Lesson 34 that have these abbreviations: La., R.I., Wis.

6. Write the three compound words from Lesson 34.

7. Write the abbreviations in Lesson 35 for the underlined words.

   Mom is (a) Doctor Smith and Dad, a nurse, is (b) Mister Smith.
   A telephone is often called a (c) , and influenza is often called (d) .
   The acronym for radio detecting and ranging is (e) .

8. Complete each sentence, using the word that means the opposite of the underlined word in the sentence.

irregular   pleasant   approximate
passenger   permission   forgotten

a. Ms. Ander was the <u>driver</u> of the car; Alex was the _____.

b. Martha doesn't do her homework at a <u>regular</u> time; she has an _____ schedule.

c. Phil is never <u>unpleasant</u>; he is always _____.

d. Ellen doesn't know the <u>exact</u> number of plants she has; she knows the _____ number.

e. Grandmother has <u>remembered</u> my birthday; Aunt Mary has _____ it.

f. Dad withdrew his <u>refusal</u> and gave me _____ to go to the movie.

Test Yourself
Find the correct spelling for each word. Write the word correctly.
1. pasenger, passenger, passanger
2. forgotten, forgotton, forgoten
3. aronotical, arinotical, aeronautical
4. vanala, vanilla, vanila
5. intellagent, intellageat, intelligent
6. plensent, pleasant, plesant

Personal Words
Write your personal words in any order you wish.

Use some of your personal words in sentences similar to those at the top of the page.

Pick five favorite or most interesting words and write them in a sentence, story, or poem.

Parts of a Dictionary Entry

(2) (3)

(1) → **snare**[1] (sner *or* snar), **1** noose for
catching small animals and
birds: *They made snares to catch
rabbits.* **2** catch with a snare: *One
day they snared a skunk.* **3** a trap: ─(4)
(5) → *Flattery is a snare in which fools
are caught.* **4** to trap. 1,3 *noun,* ←(6)
2,4 *verb,* **snared, snar ing.** ←(7)
[probably from a Scandinavian
(8) → word of the 1200s, such as
Icelandic *snara*]

(1) **The entry word**
(2) **The homograph number**
(3) **Pronunciations**
(4) **The definitions**
(5) **An illustrative sentence**
(6) **The part-of-speech label**
(7) **Inflected forms**
(8) **The word history**

Spellings of English Sounds*

SYMBOL: SPELLINGS:

a   **a**t, pl**ai**d, h**a**lf, l**au**gh
ā   **a**ble, **ai**d, s**ay**, **a**ge, **eigh**t, th**ey**, br**ea**k,
    v**ei**n, g**au**ge, cr**e**pe, ber**et**
ä   f**a**ther, **ah**, c**a**lm, h**ea**rt, baz**aa**r
b   **b**ad, ra**bb**it
ch **ch**ild, wa**tch**, fu**t**ure, ques**t**ion
d   **d**id, a**dd**, fill**ed**
e   **e**nd, s**ai**d, **ae**rial, **a**ny, br**ea**d, s**ay**s,
    h**ei**fer, l**eo**pard, fri**e**nd, b**u**ry
ē   **e**qual, **ea**t, **ee**l, happ**y**, citi**e**s, c**ei**ling,
    rec**ei**ve, k**ey**, th**e**se, bel**ie**ve, mach**i**ne,
    lit**e**r, p**eo**ple
ėr st**er**n, **ear**th, **ur**ge, f**ir**st, w**or**d, j**our**ney
f   **f**at, e**ff**ort, lau**gh**, **ph**rase

g   **g**o, e**gg**, **gu**est, **gh**ost, lea**gue**
h   **h**e, w**h**o, **j**ai alai
i   **i**t, **E**ngland, **ea**r, h**y**mn, b**ee**n, s**ie**ve,
    w**o**men, b**u**sy, b**ui**ld, w**ei**rd
ī   **I**, **i**ce, l**ie**, sk**y**, t**y**pe, r**y**e, **eye**, **i**sland,
    h**igh**, **ei**der, **ai**sle, h**eigh**t, b**uy**, c**oy**ote
j   **j**am, **g**em, exa**gg**erate, sche**d**ule,
    ba**dg**er, bri**dge**, sol**di**er, lar**ge**,
    alle**gi**ance
k   **c**oat, **k**ind, ba**ck**, e**ch**o, a**ch**e, **qu**it,
    a**cc**ount, anti**qu**e, ex**c**ite, a**cqu**ire
l   **l**and, te**ll**
m   **m**e, co**mm**on, cli**mb**, sole**mn**, pal**m**
n   **n**o, ma**nn**er, **kn**ife, **gn**aw, **pn**eumonia
ng lo**ng**, i**nk**, ha**n**dkerchief, to**ngue**
o   **o**dd, w**a**tch, **ho**nest, y**a**cht
ō   **o**pen, **oa**k, t**oe**, **ow**n, h**o**me, **oh**, f**o**lk,
    th**ough**, bur**eau**, s**ew**, br**oo**ch, s**ou**l
ô   **o**rder, **a**ll, **au**thor, **aw**ful, b**oa**rd,
    b**ough**t, w**a**lk, t**au**ght, c**ough**, Ut**ah**
oi **oi**l, b**oy**
ou **ou**t, **ow**l, b**ough**, h**our**
p   **p**ay, ha**pp**y
r   **r**un, ca**rr**y, **wr**ong, **rh**ythm
s   **s**ay, mi**ss**, **c**ent, **sc**ent, dan**c**e, ten**s**e,
    sword, pi**zz**a, li**s**ten
sh **sh**e, ma**ch**ine, **s**ure, o**c**ean, spe**ci**al,
    ten**si**on, mi**ssi**on, na**ti**on
t   **t**ell, bu**tt**on, **t**wo, **Th**omas, stopp**ed**,
    dou**bt**, recei**pt**, pizza
th **th**in
ŦH **th**en, brea**the**
u   **u**p, **o**ven, tr**ou**ble, d**oe**s, fl**oo**d
u̇ f**u**ll, g**oo**d, w**o**lf, sh**ou**ld
ü   f**oo**d, j**u**nior, r**u**le, bl**ue**, wh**o**, m**o**ve,
    thr**ew**, s**ou**p, thr**ough**, sh**oe**, t**wo**, fr**ui**t,
    man**eu**ver, li**eu**tenant, b**eau**ty, v**iew**
v   **v**ery, ha**v**e, o**f**, **St**ephen
w   **w**ill, **qu**ick
y   **y**es, opin**i**on
z   **z**ero, ha**s**, bu**zz**, **s**ci**ss**ors, **x**ylophone
zh mea**s**ure, gara**ge**, divi**si**on
ə   **a**lone, c**o**mplete, mom**e**nt, **au**thority,
    barg**ai**n, Apr**i**l, cauti**ou**s, circ**u**s

*Not all English spellings of these sounds are included in this list.

148

Full pronunciation key

a	hat, cap	**o**	hot, rock
ā	age, face	**ō**	open, go
ä	father, far	**ô**	order, all
		oi	oil, voice
		ou	house, out
b	bad, rob		
ch	child, much		
d	did, red	**p**	paper, cup
		r	run, try
		s	say, yes
e	let, best	**sh**	she, rush
ē	equal, be	**t**	tell, it
ėr	term, learn	**th**	thin, both
		ᴛʜ	then, smooth
f	fat, if		
g	go, bag	**u**	cup, butter
h	he, how	**ù**	full, put
		ü	rule, move
i	it, pin		
ī	ice, five	**v**	very, save
		w	will, woman
		y	young, yet
j	jam, enjoy	**z**	zero, breeze
k	kind, seek	**zh**	measure, seizure
l	land, coal		
m	me, am		
n	no, in	**ə**	represents:
ng	long, bring		a in about
			e in taken
			i in pencil
			o in lemon
			u in circus

ab sorb (ab sôrb′), **1** take in or suck up (liquids): *The sponge absorbed the spilled milk.* **2** take in and make part of itself: *The United States has absorbed millions of immigrants. Digested food is absorbed into the bloodstream in the intestines.* **3** take in without reflecting: *Rugs absorb sounds and make a house quieter.* **4** take up all the attention of; interest very much. *v.*

A chil les (ə kil′ēz), (in Greek legends) a hero of the Greeks at the siege of Troy. No weapon could injure Achilles anywhere, except in the heel. *n.*

ac knowl edg ment or **ac knowl edge ment** (ak nol′ij mənt), **1** something given or done to show that one has received a service, favor, gift, message, etc.: *The winner waved in acknowledgment of the crowd's cheers.* **2** act of admitting that something is true: *acknowledgment of a mistake.* **3** recognition of authority, claims, or merit. *n.*

ac ne (ak′nē), a skin disease in which the oil glands in the skin become clogged and inflamed, often causing pimples. *n.*

ad jec tive (aj′ik tiv), **1** one of a class of words that qualify, limit, or add to the meaning of a noun or pronoun. In "a tiny brook," "The day is warm," "great happiness," and "this pencil," *tiny, warm, great,* and *this* are adjectives. **2** of an adjective. **3** used as an adjective. **1** *n.,* **2,3** *adj.*

aer o nau ti cal (er′ə nô′tə kəl *or* ar′ə nô′tə kəl), of or having to do with the design, manufacture, and operation of aircraft. *adj.* —**aer′o nau′ti cal ly,** *adv.*

Af ghan (af′gən), **1** person born or living in Afghanistan. **2** of Afghanistan or its people. **3** *afghan,* blanket or shawl made of knitted or crocheted wool, nylon, etc. **1,3** *n.,* **2** *adj.*

ag gres sion (ə gresh′ən), **1** the first step in an attack or a quarrel; unprovoked attack: *A country that sends its army to occupy another country is guilty of aggression.* **2** practice of making assaults or attacks on the rights or territory of others as a method or policy. *n.*

ag ile (aj′əl), **1** moving quickly and easily; nimble: *as agile as a cat.* **2** quick in thinking; alert: *You need an agile mind to solve puzzles. adj.* —**ag′ile ly,** *adv.*

ag ri cul ture (ag′rə kul′chər), science or art of cultivating the soil, including the production of crops and the raising of livestock; farming. *n.*

an a lyze (an′l īz), **1** separate anything into its parts or elements to find out what it is made of: *The chemistry teacher analyzed water into two colorless gases, oxygen and hydrogen. Analyze this sentence by explaining the form and use of every word in it.* **2** examine carefully and in detail. *v.,* **an a lyzed, an a lyz ing.**

The contents of the glossary entries in this book have been adapted from the *Thorndike Barnhart Intermediate Dictionary,* copyright © 1974 by Scott, Foresman and Company.

an gle[1] (ang′gəl), **1** the space between two lines or surfaces that meet: *Angles are measured in degrees.* **2** the figure formed by two such lines or surfaces. **3** the difference in direction between two such lines or surfaces. **4** move, turn, or bend at an angle: *The road angles to the right here.* **5** corner: *We took a picture of the northeast angle of the school.* **6** point of view. 1-3,5,6 *n.,* 4 *v.,* **an gled, an gling.** [from French of the 1300's]

an gle[2] (ang′gəl), **1** fish with a hook and line. **2** try to get something by using tricks or schemes. *v.,* **an gled, an gling.** [Old English *angel* fishhook]

an ti bi ot ic (an′ti bī ot′ik), substance produced by a living organism that destroys or weakens germs. Penicillin is an antibiotic useful in treating scarlet fever and common types of blood poisoning. *n.*

an y way (en′ē wā), **1** in any case; at least: *I am coming anyway, no matter what you say.* **2** in any way whatever; carelessly; anyhow: *She stacked the books on the floor just anyway.* *adv.*

ar chi tec ture (är′kə tek′chər), **1** science or art of planning and designing buildings. **2** style or special manner of building: *Greek architecture made much use of columns.* **3** construction: *We admire the massive architecture of the Pyramids.* *n.*

au to mo bile (ô′tə mə bēl′), **1** a passenger vehicle, for use on roads and streets, that carries its own engine. **2** of or for automobiles: *an automobile mechanic.* 1 *n.,* 2 *adj.*

bac ter i a (bak tir′ē ə), very tiny and simple plants, so small that they can usually be seen only through a microscope. Bacteria consist of single cells that are rod-shaped, spherical, or spiral, and have no chlorophyll. Certain bacteria cause diseases such as pneumonia and typhoid fever; others do useful things, such as turning cider into vinegar. *n.pl. of* **bacterium.**

ban jo (ban′jō), a musical instrument having four or five strings, played by plucking the strings with the fingers or with a plectrum. It has a head and neck like a guitar and a body like a tambourine. *n., pl.* **ban jos** or **ban joes.** [apparently from a Bantu word]

banjo—Tightly stretched skin over the round body increases the sound made by plucking the strings.

Ban tu (ban′tü), **1** member of a large group of Negro tribes living in central and southern Africa. **2** any of the languages of these tribes. **3** of these tribes or their languages. 1,2 *n., pl.* **Ban tu** or **Ban tus,** 3 *adj.*

ba zaar or **ba zar** (bə zär′), **1** street or streets full of small shops and booths in Oriental countries. **2** place for the sale of many kinds of goods. **3** sale of things contributed by various people, held for some charity or other special purpose. *n.*

bill of sale, a document transferring ownership of something from the seller to the buyer.

bloom ers (blü′mərz), **1** loose trousers, gathered at the knee, formerly worn by women and girls for physical training. **2** underwear made like these. *n.pl.* [from Amelia J. *Bloomer,* 1818-1894, who first referred to them]

bo lo gna (bə lō′nē *or* bə lō′nə), a large sausage usually made of beef, veal, and pork. *n., pl.* **bo lo gnas.**

booth (büth), **1** a covered stall or similar place where goods are sold or shown at a fair, market, convention, etc. **2** a small, closed place for a telephone, motion-picture projector, etc. **3** a small, closed place for voting at elections. **4** a partly enclosed space in a restaurant or café, containing a table and seats for a few persons. *n., pl.* **booths** (büŦHz *or* büths). [from Scandinavian (Old Dutch) *bōth*]

brown ish (brou′nish), somewhat brown, a dark color like that of toast, potato skins, or coffee. *adj.*

busi ness (biz′nis), **1** thing that one is busy at; work; occupation: *A carpenter's business is building.* **2** matter; affair; concern: *I am tired of the whole business.* **3** buying and selling; commercial dealings; trade. **4** of or having to do with business. **5** a store, factory, or other commercial enterprise; industrial establishment. 1-3,5 *n., pl.* **busi ness es** for 5; 4 *adj.*

caf tan (kaf′tən *or* käf tän′), a long-sleeved, ankle-length tunic worn by men in Turkey, Egypt, etc. *n.* [from Turkish *kaftan*]

cap i tal (kap′ə təl), **1** city where the government of a country, state, or province is located. Toronto is the capital of Ontario. Lincoln is the capital of Nebraska. **2** capital letter. A capital is used at the beginning of a sentence or a proper name. *n.*

Cap i tol (kap′ə təl), **1** the building at Washington, D.C., in which Congress meets. **2** Also, **capitol.** the building in which a state legislature meets. *n.*

cash mere (kash′mir *or* kazh′mir), a fine, soft wool, used in making sweaters, coats, etc. The finest cashmere is obtained from a breed of long-haired goats of Tibet and Kashmir. *n.*

cas se role (kas′ə rōl′), **1** a covered baking dish in which food can be both cooked and served. **2** food cooked and served in such a dish: *My favorite meal is a casserole of chicken and rice. n.*

check mate (chek′māt′), **1** in chess: **a** put (an opponent's king) in check from which his next move cannot free him, and so win the game. **b** a move that ends the game by putting the opponent's king in check so that he is unable to escape by his next move. **2** defeat completely. **3** a complete defeat. 1a, 2 *v.*, **check mat ed, check mat ing;** 1b, 3 *n.* [from Persian *shāh māt* the king is dead]

cho les te rol (kə les′tə rol′ *or* kə les′tər ōl′), a white, fatty substance, found in the blood and tissues of the body and also in foods such as eggs and meat. It is important in metabolism. *n.*

cin cho na (sin kō′nə), **1** an evergreen tree native to the Andes Mountains, now also grown in the East Indies. It is valuable for its bark. **2** its bitter bark, from which quinine and other drugs are obtained; Peruvian bark. *n.,pl.* **cin cho nas.** [from Countess *Cinchón,* wife of a Spanish viceroy to Peru]

clas sic (klas′ik), **1** author or artist of acknowledged excellence whose works serve as a standard, model, or guide. **2** work of literature or art of the highest rank or quality. *n.*

cm., centimeter or centimeters.

co a li tion (kō′ə lish′ən), **1** union; combination. **2** alliance of statesmen, political parties, etc., for some special purpose. In wartime several countries may form a temporary coalition against a common enemy. *n.*

col lab o rate (kə lab′ə rāt′), **1** work together: *The two authors collaborated in writing a history of the United States.* **2** aid or cooperate with enemies of one's country: *The traitor collaborated with the enemy. v.,* **col lab o rat ed, col lab o rat ing.**

com mer cial (kə mėr′shəl), **1** having to do with trade or business: *a store or other commercial establishment.* **2** made to be sold for a profit: *Anything you can buy in a store is a commercial product.* **3** an advertising message on radio or television, broadcast between or during programs. 1,2 *adj.*, 3 *n.* —**com mer′cial ly,** *adv.*

com par a tive (kəm par′ə tiv), **1** measured by comparison with something else; relative. **2** the second of three degrees of comparison of an adjective or adverb. *Fairer* is the comparative of *fair. More slowly* is the comparative of *slowly.* 1 *adj.*, 2 *n.*

con do min i um (kon′də min′ē əm), apartment house in which each apartment is purchased as a piece of real estate and separately valued for property tax purposes. *n.* [from Latin *com-* with + *dominium* lordship]

a hat	i it	oi oil	ch child	⎧ a in about
ā age	ī ice	ou out	ng long	⎪ e in taken
ä far	o hot	u cup	sh she	ə = ⎨ i in pencil
e let	ō open	u̇ put	th thin	⎪ o in lemon
ē equal	ô order	ü rule	⧲ then	⎩ u in circus
ėr term			zh measure	

con flict (kon′flikt *for 1,2;* kən flikt′ *for 3*), **1** a fight or struggle, especially a long one: *The conflict between Greece and Troy lasted for ten years.* **2** active opposition of persons or ideas; clash. **3** be actively opposed; differ in thought or action; clash: *The testimony of the witnesses conflicted on whether or not the robber had blond or dark hair.* 1,2 *n.*, 3 *v.*

con gru ent (kən grü′ənt *or* kong′grü ənt), **1** exactly coinciding: *Congruent triangles have the same size and shape.* **2** congruous. *adj.*

con junc tion (kən jungk′shən), **1** word that connects words, phrases, clauses, or sentences. *And, but, or, though,* and *if* are conjunctions. **2** a joining together; union; combination: *Our school, in conjunction with two other schools, will hold a large bazaar next week. n.*

con ta gious (kən tā′jəs), **1** spreading by contact: *Scarlet fever is a contagious disease.* **2** easily spreading from one person to another: *Yawning is often contagious. adj.* —**con ta′gious ly,** *adv.*

con tam i nate (kən tam′ə nāt), make impure by contact; defile; pollute: *The drinking water had been contaminated by sewage. v.,* **con tam i nat ed, con tam i nat ing.**

co pra (kō′prə), the dried meat of coconuts. Coconut oil is obtained from copra. *n.*

cor net (kôr net′), a musical wind instrument somewhat like a trumpet, usually made of brass. It has three valves that control the pitch. *n.*

co ro net (kôr′ə net′), **1** a small crown worn as a mark of high rank: *The king wore a crown; the prince wore a coronet.* **2** a circle of gold, jewels, or flowers worn around the head as an ornament. *n.*

coun cil (koun′səl), **1** group of people called together to give advice and to discuss or settle questions. **2** group of persons elected by citizens to make laws for and manage a city or town. *n.*

cream (krēm), **1** the oily, yellowish part of milk. Butter is made from cream. **2** a fancy sweet dessert or candy made of cream: *chocolate creams.* **3** cook with cream, milk, or a sauce made of cream or milk with butter and flour. **4** make into a smooth mixture like cream: *I creamed the butter and sugar together for a cake.* **5** the best or choicest part of anything: *the cream of the crop.* 1,2,5 *n.*, 3,4 *v.*

cro chet (krō shā′), **1** knit (sweaters, lace, etc.) with a single needle having a hook at one end. **2** knitting done in this way. 1 *v.*, **cro cheted** (krō shād′), **cro chet ing** (krō shā′ing); 2 *n.* [from Old French, diminutive of *croche* hook]

crys tal (kris′tl), **1** a clear, transparent mineral that looks like ice. It is a kind of quartz. **2** piece of crystal cut into form for use or ornament. **3** clear and transparent like crystal: *crystal spring water.* **4** a very transparent glass from which drinking glasses, serving dishes, etc., are made. **5** made of crystal. **6** the transparent glass or plastic cover of a watch dial. 1,2,4,6 *n.*, 3,5 *adj.*

cul ti va tion (kul′tə vā′shən), **1** act of preparing land and growing crops by plowing, planting, and necessary care: *Better cultivation of soil will result in better crops.* **2** condition of being prepared by plowing, planting, etc. **3** act of giving time and thought to improving and developing (the body, mind, or manners). **4** result of improvement or growth through education and experience; culture. *n.*

cur i um (kyur′ē əm), a radioactive metallic element produced artificially from plutonium or uranium. *n.* [from Marie and Pierre *Curie*]

cy cle (sī′kəl), **1** period of time or complete process of growth or action that repeats itself in the same order. The seasons of the year—spring, summer, autumn, and winter—make a cycle. **2** bicycle, tricycle, or motorcycle. **3** ride a bicycle, tricycle, or motorcycle. 1,2 *n.*, 3 *v.*, **cy cled, cy cling.**

czar (zär), **1** emperor. It was the title of the former emperors of Russia. **2** person having absolute power. *n.* Also, **tsar** or **tzar.**

daf fo dil (daf′ə dil), **1** plant with long, slender leaves and yellow flowers that bloom in the spring. It grows from a bulb. **2** its flower. *n.*

dec a me ter (dek′ə mē′tər), unit of length equal to 10 meters. *n.*

de ceit (di sēt′), **1** a making a person believe as true something that is false; deceiving; lying: *An honest person is incapable of deceit.* **2** a dishonest trick; lie spoken or acted. **3** quality in a person that makes him tell lies or cheat; deceitfulness: *The dishonest trader was full of deceit. n.*

dis clo sure (dis klō′zhər), **1** an opening to view: *disclosure of a secret.* **2** thing made known: *The newspaper's disclosures shocked the public. n.*

dis grun tled (dis grunt′ld), in bad humor; discontented. *adj.*

dis pute (dis pyüt′), **1** give reasons or facts for or against something; argue; debate; discuss:

Congress disputed over the need for new taxes. **2** argument; debate: *There is a dispute between the taxpayers and the mayor over where to build the new school.* **3** quarrel: *The children disputed over the last piece of cake.* **4** fight for; fight over. 1,3,4 *v.*, **dis put ed, dis put ing;** 2 *n.*

dis si pate (dis′ə pāt), **1** spread in different directions; scatter so as to disappear or cause to disappear; disperse; dispel: *After a brisk morning wind dissipated the clouds, the sky was clear all day.* **2** spend foolishly; waste on things of little value: *In a very short time I had dissipated my inheritance. v.*, **dis si pat ed, dis si pat ing.**

dkg., decagram or decagrams.

dom i nant (dom′ə nənt), **1** most powerful or influential; controlling; ruling; governing: *The principal was the dominant figure at the P.T.A. meeting.* **2** rising high above its surroundings; towering over. *adj.*

dram (dram), a small weight. In apothecaries' weight, 8 drams make one ounce; in avoirdupois weight, 16 drams make one ounce. *n.*

dur a ble (dur′ə bəl *or* dyur′ə bəl), **1** able to withstand wear. **2** lasting a long time. *adj.*

e lec tron (i lek′tron), a tiny particle carrying one unit of negative electricity. All atoms have electrons arranged about a nucleus. *n.*

em-[1], *prefix.* form of **en-**[1] before *b, p,* and sometimes *m,* as in *embark, employ.*

em-[2], *prefix.* form of **en-**[2] before *b, m, p, ph,* as in *emblem, emphasis.*

em broi der y (em broi′dər ē), **1** act or art of sewing (cloth, leather, etc.) with a raised design or pattern of stitches. **2** embroidered work or material; ornamental designs sewn in cloth, leather, etc., with a needle. *n., pl.* **em broi der ies.**

em ploy (em ploi′), **1** give work and pay to: *That big factory employs many workers.* **2** service for pay; employment: *There are many workers in the employ of that big factory.* 1 *v.*, 2 *n.*

en-[1], *prefix.* **1** cause to be ____ ; make ____ : *Enfeeble = make feeble.* **2** put in ____ ; put on ____ : *Enthrone = put on a throne.* **3** other meanings, as in *enact, encourage, entwine.* The addition of *en-* rarely changes the meaning of a verb except to make it more emphatic. See also **em-**[1]. [from Old French from Latin *in-*]

en-[2], *prefix.* in; on, as in *energy.* See also **em-**[2]. [from Greek]

en close (en klōz′), **1** shut in on all sides; surround: *The little park was enclosed by tall apartment buildings.* **2** put a wall or fence around. **3** put in an envelope along with a letter, etc. *v.*, **en closed, en clos ing.** Also, **inclose.**

en dur ance (en dùr′əns *or* en dyùr′əns), **1** power to last and to withstand hard wear: *A runner must have great endurance to run 30 miles in a day.* **2** power to stand something without giving out; holding out; bearing up: *Her endurance of pain is remarkable. n.*

en grave (en grāv′), **1** cut deeply in; carve in an artistic way. **2** cut (a picture, design, map, etc.) in lines on a metal plate, block of wood, etc., for printing. **3** print from such a plate, block, etc. **4** fix firmly: *Her face is engraved in my mind. v.,* **en graved, en grav ing.**

en trust (en trust′), **1** charge with a trust: *We entrusted the class treasurer with all the money for bus fares on our class trip.* **2** give the care of; hand over for safekeeping. *v.* Also, **intrust.**

e qui lat er al (ē′kwə lat′ər əl), having all sides equal. *adj.* —**e′qui lat′er al ly,** *adv.*

equilateral triangle

ex ag ge ra tion (eg zaj′ə rā′shən), a statement that goes beyond the truth or enlarges beyond what is normal: *It is an exaggeration to say that you would rather die than touch a snake. n.*

ex cel lent (ek′sə lənt), of unusually good quality; better than others; superior: *Excellent work deserves high praise. adj.* —**ex′cel lent ly,** *adv.*

ex ec u tive (eg zek′yə tiv), **1** having to do with carrying out or managing affairs: *The head of a school has an executive position.* **2** person who carries out or manages affairs. **3** having the duty and power of putting the laws into effect: *The President of the United States is the head of the executive branch of the government.* 1,3 *adj.,* 2 *n.*

ex pert (ek′spėrt′ *for 1;* ek spėrt′ *or* ek′spėrt′ *for 2*), **1** a very skillful person; person who knows a great deal about some special thing. **2** requiring or showing special skill: *expert workmanship, expert testimony.* 1 *n.,* 2 *adj.* —**ex pert′ly,** *adv.*

ex ploit (ek′sploit *for 1;* ek sploit′ *for 2*), **1** a bold, unusual act; daring deed: *This book tells about the exploits of Robin Hood.* **2** make unfair or selfish use of: *Nations used to exploit their colonies, taking as much wealth out of them as they could.* 1 *n.,* 2 *v.* —**ex ploit′er,** *n.*

fel low (fel′ō), **1** a male person; man or boy. **2** a person; anybody; one. **3** dog, horse, etc., addressed in a friendly way. **4** being in the same or a like condition, class, etc.: *fellow citizens, fellow sufferers.* 1-3 *n.,* 4 *adj.*

Fer ris wheel (fer′is), a large, revolving wheel with seats hanging from its rim, used in carnivals,

a hat	**i** it	**oi** oil	**ch** child	⎧ a in about
ā age	**ī** ice	**ou** out	**ng** long	⎪ e in taken
ä far	**o** hot	**u** cup	**sh** she	ə = ⎨ i in pencil
e let	**ō** open	**ů** put	**th** thin	⎪ o in lemon
ē equal	**ô** order	**ü** rule	**ŦH** then	⎩ u in circus
ėr term			**zh** measure	

amusement parks, at fairs, etc. [from George *Ferris,* 1859-1896, American inventor]

fer ti lize (fėr′tl īz), **1** make fertile; make able to produce much. **2** unite with (an egg cell) in fertilization; impregnate. **3** put fertilizer on: *fertilize a lawn. v.,* **fer ti lized, fer ti liz ing.**

fes ti val (fes′tə vəl), **1** day or special time of rejoicing or feasting, often in memory of some great happening: *Christmas is a Christian festival; Hanukkah is a Jewish festival.* **2** celebration or entertainment. *n.*

feu dal (fyü′dl), of or having to do with feudalism: *the feudal system, feudal laws. adj.*

feu dal ism (fyü′dl iz′əm), the social, economic, and political system of Europe in the Middle Ages. Under this system vassals gave military and other services to their lord in return for his protection and the use of land. *n.*

flash back (flash′bak′), a break in the continuous series of events of a novel, motion picture, etc., to introduce some earlier event or scene. *n.*

fledg ling or **fledge ling** (flej′ling), **1** a young bird just able to fly. **2** a young, inexperienced person. *n.*

fowl (foul), **1** any bird. **2** any of several kinds of large birds used for food. **3** flesh of a fowl used for food. *n., pl.* **fowls** or **fowl.**

fund (fund), **1** sum of money set aside for a special purpose: *The school has a fund of $2000 to buy books with.* **2** **funds,** *pl.* money ready to use: *Do you have the funds to take this trip? n.*

fur long (fėr′lông), measure of distance equal to one eighth of a mile; 220 yards. *n.*

gas o line or **gas o lene** (gas′ə lēn′ *or* gas′ə lēn′), a colorless, liquid mixture which evaporates and burns very easily. It is made from petroleum or from gas formed in the earth. Gasoline is used chiefly as a fuel to run automobiles, airplanes, and motorboats. *n.*

ge net ic (jə net′ik), **1** having to do with origin and natural growth. **2** of or having to do with genetics. *adj.*

ge ra ni um (jə rā′nē əm), plant with fragrant leaves and large clusters of showy flowers, often grown in pots for window plants. *n.*

ghet to (get′ō), **1** (formerly) a part of a city where Jews were required to live. **2** part of a city where any racial or other minority group lives. *n., pl.* **ghet tos.**

gong (gông), a large piece of metal shaped like a bowl or a saucer which makes a loud noise when struck. A gong is a kind of bell. *n.* [from Malay]

good-by (gud′bī′), farewell: *We say "Good-by" to friends when they go away. interj., n., pl.* **good-bys.**

good-bye (gud′bī′), good-by. *interj., n., pl.* **good-byes.**

gorge (gôrj), **1** a deep, narrow valley, usually steep and rocky, especially one with a stream. **2** eat greedily until full; stuff with food. **1** *n.,* **2** *v.,* **gorged, gorg ing.**

graf fi ti (grə fē′tē), drawings or writings scratched or scribbled on a wall or other surface. *n.pl.* of **graf fi to** (grə fē′tō).

gram (gram), unit of weight or mass in the metric system. Twenty-eight grams weigh about one ounce. *n.* Also, **gramme.**

hai ku (hī′kü), a poem of three lines and containing only 17 syllables. *n., pl.* **hai ku.**

hap haz ard (hap haz′ərd), not planned; random: *Haphazard answers are often wrong. adj.* —**hap haz′ard ly,** *adv.*

har row (har′ō), **1** a heavy frame with iron teeth or upright disks. Harrows are used by farmers to break up plowed ground into finer pieces or to cover seeds with earth. **2** draw a harrow over (land, etc.). **1** *n.,* **2** *v.*

head quar ters (hed′kwôr′tərz), **1** place from which the chief or commanding officer of an army, police force, etc., sends out orders. **2** place from which any organization is controlled and directed; main office. *n. pl. or sing.*

he red i ty (hə red′ə tē), **1** the passing on of physical or mental characteristics from parent to offspring by means of genes. **2** qualities of body and mind that have come to offspring from parents. *n., pl.* **he red i ties.**

hex a gon (hek′sə gon), a plane figure having six angles and six sides. *n.*

regular hexagon   **irregular hexagon**

hol low (hol′ō), **1** having nothing, or only air, inside; with a hole inside; not solid; empty: *A tube or pipe is hollow.* **2** shaped like a bowl or cup. **3** a hollow place; hole: *a hollow in the road.* **4** a low place between hills; valley: *Sleepy Hollow.* **1,2** *adj.,* **3,4** *n.*

hy a cinth (hī′ə sinth), **1** plant of the same family as the lily, that grows from a bulb and has a spike of small, fragrant, bell-shaped flowers. **2** its flower. *n.*

il lu mi nate (i lü′mə nāt), **1** light up; make bright: *The room was illuminated by four large lamps. The big searchlight illuminates a spot a mile away.* **2** make clear; explain: *Our teacher could illuminate almost any subject we studied.* **3** decorate with lights: *The streets were illuminated for the celebration.* **4** decorate with gold, colors, pictures, and designs. *v.,* **il lu mi nat ed, il lu mi nat ing.**

im-, *prefix.* form of **in-¹** before *b, m,* and *p,* as in *imbibe, immoral, impatient.*

in-¹, *prefix.* not; the opposite of; the absence of: *Inexpensive = not expensive. Inattention = the absence of attention.* Also, **il-, im-, ir-.** [from Latin]

in-², *prefix.* in; into; on; upon: *Incase = (put) into a case. Intrust = (give) in trust.* [from Latin *in-,* from *in,* prep.]

in-³, *prefix.* in; within; into; toward: *Indoors = within doors. Inland = toward land.* [Old English]

in close (in klōz′), enclose. *v.,* **in closed, in clos ing.**

in ter jec tion (in′tər jek′shən), an exclamation showing emotion. It is regarded as a part of speech. *Oh! ah! alas!* and *hurrah!* are interjections. *n.*

in ter view (in′tər vyü), **1** a meeting, generally of persons face to face, to talk over something special. **2** a meeting between a reporter and a person from whom information is sought for publication or broadcast. **3** newspaper or magazine article, or broadcast containing the information given at such a meeting. **4** have an interview with; meet and talk with, especially to obtain information. **1-3** *n.,* **4** *v.* —**in′ter view′er,** *n.*

in trust (in trust′), entrust. *v.*

ir-¹, *prefix.* the form of **in-¹** before *r,* as in *irrational, irregular.*

ir-², *prefix.* the form of **in-²** before *r,* as in *irrigate.*

i so tope (ī′sə tōp), any of two or more forms of a chemical element that have the same chemical properties and the same atomic number (number of protons), but different atomic weights (number of neutrons). Hydrogen and heavy hydrogen are isotopes. *n.*

-ive, *suffix forming adjectives from nouns.* **1** of or having to do with, as in *interrogative, inductive.* **2** tending to; likely to, as in *active, appreciative.* [from French *-ive* (feminine of *-if* from Latin *-ivus*) or directly from Latin]

jai a lai (hī′ ä lī′), game similar to handball, played on a walled court with a hard ball, popular in Spain and Latin America. The ball is caught and thrown with a kind of curved wicker basket fastened to the arm. [from Spanish *jai* festival + *alai* merry]

junc tion (jungk′shən), **1** a joining or a being joined. **2** place of joining or meeting. *n.*

kay ak (kī′ak), **1** an Eskimo canoe made of skins stretched over a light frame of wood or bone with an opening in the middle for a person. **2** a similar craft of other material. *n.* Also, **kaiak.**

kayak—The paddle has a blade at each end; first one blade is dipped in the water, then the other.

ki lom e ter (kə lom′ə tər *or* kil′ə mē′tər), measure of length equal to 1000 meters, or 3280.8 feet. *n.*

ki mo no (kə mō′nə), **1** a loose outer garment held in place by a sash, worn by Japanese men and women. **2** a woman's loose dressing gown. *n., pl.* **ki mo nos.** [from Japanese]

kl., kiloliter or kiloliters.

kohl ra bi (kōl′rä′bē), **1** plant related to the cabbage and having a turnip-shaped stem. **2** its stem, which is eaten as a vegetable. *n., pl.* **kohl ra bies.**

league[1] (lēg), **1** a union of persons, parties, or nations formed to help one another. **2** unite in a league; form a union. **3** association of sports clubs or teams: *a baseball league.* **1,3** *n.,* **2** *v.,* **leagued, lea guing.** [from French of the 1400's *ligue,* ultimately from Latin *ligare* to bind]

league[2] (lēg), measure of distance equal to about 3 miles. *n.* [from Latin *leuga*]

lei sure (lē′zhər), **1** time free from required work in which a person may rest, amuse himself, and

a hat	i it	oi oil	ch child		a in about
ā age	ī ice	ou out	ng long		e in taken
ä far	o hot	u cup	sh she	ə =	i in pencil
e let	ō open	u̇ put	th thin		o in lemon
ē equal	ô order	ü rule	ᴛʜ then		u in circus
ėr term			zh measure		

do the things he likes to do. **2** free; not busy: *leisure hours.* **1** *n.,* **2** *adj.*

li a ble (lī′ə bəl), **1** likely; unpleasantly likely: *That glass is liable to break.* **2** in danger of having, doing, etc. **3** responsible; under obligation; bound by law to pay. *adj.*

lim ber (lim′bər), **1** bending easily; flexible. **2** make or become limber: *He is stiff when he begins to skate, but limbers up quickly.* **1** *adj.,* **2** *v.*

lin e ar (lin′ē ər), **1** of a line or lines; in a line or lines: *The royal crown is passed from father to son in a linear succession.* **2** made of lines; making use of lines: *linear designs.* **3** of length: *An inch is a linear measure.* **4** like a line; long and narrow: *A pine tree has linear leaves. adj.*

liq uid (lik′wid), **1** substance that is not a solid or a gas; substance that flows freely like water. Mercury is a liquid at room temperature. **2** in the form of a liquid; melted: *liquid soap.* **1** *n.,* **2** *adj.*

li ter (lē′tər), the basic measure of volume in the metric system; 1.0567 quarts liquid measure, or .908 quart dry measure. A liter is the volume of one kilogram of water. *n.* Also, **litre.**

loc. cit., in the place cited [for Latin *loco citato*].

mac ra mé (mak′rə mä), a coarse lace or fringe made by knotting thread or cord in patterns. *n.* [from Turkish *makrama* napkin]

mag a zine (mag′ə zēn′ *or* mag′ə zēn′), **1** a publication issued at regular intervals, especially weekly or monthly, which contains stories, articles, photographs, etc., by various contributors. **2** a room or building for storing gunpowder, guns, food, or other military supplies. *n.*

ma neu ver (mə nü′vər), **1** a planned movement of troops or warships. **2** a skillful plan or movement; clever trick: *When we refused to use his idea, he tried to force it on us by a series of maneuvers.* **3** to force by skillful plans; get by clever tricks. **4** move or manipulate skillfully: *I maneuvered the car through the heavy traffic with ease.* **1,2** *n.,* **3,4** *v.* Also, **manoeuvre.**

mar i gold (mar′ə gōld), **1** plant of the same family as the aster, with yellow, orange, brownish, or red flowers. **2** its flower. *n.*

marsh mal low (märsh/mal/ō *or* märsh/mel/ō), a soft, white, spongy candy, covered with powdered sugar. *n.*

marsh mallow, kind of mallow with pink flowers that grows in marshy places.

me men to (mə men/tō), something serving as a reminder, warning, or remembrance: *These post cards are mementos of our trip abroad.* n., pl. **me men tos** or **me men toes.**

me te o rite (mē/tē ə rīt/), mass of stone or metal that has fallen to the earth from outer space; a fallen meteor. *n.*

me ter[1] (mē/tər), **1** the basic measure of length in the metric system. A meter is equal to 39.37 inches. **2** any kind of poetic rhythm; the arrangement of beats or accents in a line of poetry. **3** musical rhythm; the arrangement of beats in music. *n.* Also, **metre.** [from French *mètre,* from Latin *metrum* measure, from Greek *metron*]

me ter[2] (mē/tər), device that measures, or measures and records, the amount of gas, water, electricity, etc., used: *an electric meter. n.* [*mete* (Old English *metan* to measure) + *-er*]

min i a ture (min/ē ə chúr *or* min/ə chər), **1** anything represented on a small scale: *In the museum there is a miniature of the ship "Mayflower."* **2** done or made on a very small scale; tiny. **3** a very small painting, usually a portrait on ivory. 1,3 *n.,* 2 *adj.*

ml., milliliter or milliliters.

mod i fi er (mod/ə fī/ər), **1** word or group of words that limits the meaning of another word or group of words. In "a very tight coat," the adjective *tight* is a modifier of *coat,* and the adverb *very* is a modifier of *tight.* **2** person or thing that modifies. *n.*

mon ar chy (mon/ər kē), **1** government by a monarch. **2** nation governed by a monarch. n., pl. **mon ar chies.**

mon soon (mon sün/), **1** a seasonal wind of the Indian Ocean and southern Asia. **2** the rainy season during which this wind blows from the southwest. *n.*

nar ra tive (nar/ə tiv), **1** story; tale. **2** narration; story-telling. **3** that narrates: *"Hiawatha" is a narrative poem.* 1,2 *n.,* 3 *adj.*

nee dle (nē/dl), **1** a very slender tool, pointed at one end and with a hole or eye to pass a thread through, used in sewing. **2** a slender rod used in knitting. **3** rod with a hook at one end used in crocheting, etc. **4** a thin steel pointer on a compass or on electrical machinery. **5** a very slender steel tube with a sharp point at one end. It is used at the end of a hypodermic syringe for injecting a liquid below the skin, or at the end of a rubber tube for extracting a liquid from the body. **6** the small, pointed piece of metal in a phonograph which picks up and transmits the vibrations from the record. **7** the needle-shaped leaf of a fir tree or pine tree. **8** INFORMAL. vex by repeated sharp prods, gibes, etc.; goad or incite. 1-7 *n.,* 8 *v.,* **nee dled, nee dling.**

neu tral (nü/trəl *or* nyü/trəl), on neither side in a quarrel or war. *adj.*

nos tal gia (no stal/jə), a painful or wistful yearning for one's home, country, city, or for anything far removed in space or time. *n.*

noth ing (nuth/ing), **1** not anything; no thing: *Nothing arrived by mail.* **2** thing that does not exist: *create a world out of nothing.* **3** thing of no importance or value; person of no importance. **4** zero; naught. **5** not at all. 1-4 *n.,* 5 *adv.*

o a sis (ō ā/sis), **1** a fertile spot in the desert where there is water and some vegetation. **2** any fertile spot in a barren land; any pleasant place in a desolate region. n., pl. **o a ses** (ō ā/sēz/).

oasis

oat meal (ōt/mēl/), **1** oats made into meal; ground or rolled oats. **2** a cooked cereal made from oatmeal. *n.*

ob-, *prefix.* **1** against; in the way; opposing; hindering, as in *obstruct.* **2** inversely; contrary to the usual position, as in *oblate.* **3** toward; to, as in *obvert.* **4** on; over, as in *obscure.* [from Latin]

o boe (ō/bō), a woodwind instrument in which a thin, high-pitched tone is produced by a double reed. *n.*

op-, *prefix.* form of *ob-* before *p,* as in *oppress.*

o paque (ō pāk/), **1** not letting light through; not transparent: *Muddy water is opaque.* **2** not shining; dark; dull. **3** obscure; hard to understand. **4** stupid. *adj.*

op. cit., in the book, etc., referred to [for Latin *opere citato*].

o ver whelm (ō/vər hwelm/), **1** overcome completely; crush: *overwhelm with grief.* **2** cover completely as a flood would: *A great wave overwhelmed the boat. v.*

pais ley (pāz/lē), having a detailed and colorful pattern: *a paisley shirt. adj.*

Pan the on (pan/thē on), temple for all the gods, built at Rome about 27 B.C. and later used as a Christian church. *n.*

par a lyze (par/ə līz), **1** affect with a lessening or loss of the power of motion or feeling: *Her left arm was paralyzed.* **2** make powerless or helplessly inactive; cripple; stun; deaden: *Fear paralyzed my mind. v.,* **par a lyzed, par a lyz ing.** Also, **paralyse.**

Par the non (pär/thə non), temple of Athena on the Acropolis in Athens, regarded as the finest example of Doric architecture. *n.*

pas tra mi (pə strä/mē), a smoked and well-seasoned cut of beef, especially a shoulder cut. *n.*

pen e trate (pen/ə trāt), **1** get into or through: *The bullet penetrated this wall, and two inches into the one beyond.* **2** pierce through; make a way: *Our eyes could not penetrate the darkness.* **3** soak through; spread through: *The rain penetrated our clothes. v.,* **pen e trat ed, pen e trat ing.**

per sua sive (pər swā/siv), able, intended, or fitted to win over to do or believe: *The salesman had a very persuasive way of talking. adj.*
—**per sua/sive ly,** *adv.* —**per sua/sive ness,** *n.*

phys ics (fiz/iks), science that deals with matter and energy and the relationships between them. Physics includes the study of force, motion, mechanics, heat, light, sound, electricity, and atomic energy. *n.*

pi (pī), the Greek letter π, used as the symbol for the ratio of the circumference of any circle to its diameter. π = 3.141592 +. *n., pl.* **pis.**

pic co lo (pik/ə lō), a small, shrill flute, sounding an octave higher than an ordinary flute. *n., pl.* **pic co los.**

po lo (pō/lō), game like hockey, played on horseback with long-handled mallets and a wooden ball. *n.* [perhaps from Tibetan *pulu*]

pred i cate (pred/ə kit), **1** (in grammar) the word or words expressing what is said about the subject. EXAMPLES: Dogs *bark.* The dogs *dug holes.* The dogs *are beagles.* **2** (in grammar) belonging to the predicate. In "Horses are strong," *strong* is a **predicate adjective.** In "The dogs are beagles," *beagles* is a **predicate noun.** *n.*

prep o si tion (prep/ə zish/ən), word that expresses some relation to a noun, pronoun, phrase, or clause which follows it. *With, for, by,* and *in* are prepositions in the sentence "A man *with* rugs *for* sale walked *by* our house *in* the morning." *n.*

prin ci pal (prin/sə pəl), **1** most important; main; chief: *Chicago is the principal city of Illinois.* **2** the head, or one of the heads, of an elementary or secondary school. 1 *adj.,* 2 *n.*

a hat	i it	oi oil	ch child	⎧ a in about
ā age	ī ice	ou out	ng long	e in taken
ä far	o hot	u cup	sh she	ə = ⎨ i in pencil
e let	ō open	u̇ put	th thin	o in lemon
ē equal	ô order	ü rule	ᵬH then	⎩ u in circus
ėr term			zh measure	

prin ci ple (prin/sə pəl), **1** a truth that is a foundation for other truths: *the principles of democratic government.* **2** a fundamental belief: *religious principles.* **3** a rule of action or conduct: *I make it a principle to save some money each week. n.*

prism (priz/əm), **1** a solid whose bases or ends have the same size and shape and are parallel to one another, and each of whose sides has two pairs of parallel edges. **2** a transparent solid, often of glass, having the shape of a prism, usually with three-sided ends. A prism separates white light passing through it into the colors of the spectrum. *n.*

prism

pro tein (prō/tēn), one of the substances containing nitrogen which are a necessary part of the cells of animals and plants. Meat, milk, cheese, eggs, and beans contain protein. *n.*

pur suit (pər süt/), a pursuing; chase: *The dog is in pursuit of the cat. n.*

pyr a mid (pir/ə mid), **1** a solid having a polygon for a base and triangular sides which meet in a point. **2** anything having the form of a pyramid. *n.*

py thon (pī/thon), any of several large snakes of Asia, Africa, and Australia that are related to the boas and kill their prey by squeezing. *n.*

rack et (rak/it), **1** an oval wooden or metal frame strung with netting and having a long handle, used to hit the ball in tennis, squash, badminton, etc. **2** a paddle-shaped wooden implement with a short handle, used to hit the ball in table tennis. *n.* Also, **racquet.** [from French of the 1500's *raquette,* from Arabic *rāha* palm of the hand]

rac quet (rak/it), racket. *n.*

ra di a tion (rā/dē ā/shən), **1** act or process of giving out light, heat, or other radiant energy. **2** energy radiated. **3** radioactive ray or rays emitted by the atoms and molecules of a radioactive substance as a result of the disintegration of atomic nuclei. Radiation is harmful to living tissue. *n.*

rav i o li (rav′ē ō′lē), small, thin pieces of dough filled with chopped meat, cheese, etc. Ravioli is cooked by boiling in water, and is usually served with a highly seasoned tomato sauce. *n. sing. or pl.*

re buke (ri byük′), 1 express disapproval of; reprove. 2 expression of disapproval; scolding. 1 *v.*, **re buked, re buk ing;** 2 *n.*

re but (ri but′), oppose by evidence on the other side or by argument; try to disprove: *rebut the argument of the other team in a debate. v.,* **re but ted, re but ting.**

re ceipt (ri sēt′), 1 a written statement that money, a package, a letter, etc., has been received. 2 write on (a bill, etc.) that something has been received or paid for. 1 *n.*, 2 *v.*

re cip ro cal (ri sip′rə kəl), 1 in return: *Although she gave me a present, she expected no reciprocal gift from me.* 2 existing on both sides; mutual. *adj.*

re fute (ri fyüt′), show (a claim, opinion, or argument) to be false or incorrect; prove wrong; disprove. *v.*, **re fut ed, re fut ing.**

re in force (rē′in fôrs′), 1 strengthen with new force or materials: *reinforce an army, reinforce a bridge.* 2 strengthen: *reinforce an argument. v.,* **re in forced, re in forc ing.** Also, **reenforce** or **re-enforce.**

rep re sent a tive (rep′ri zen′tə tiv), 1 person appointed or elected to act or speak for others: *He is the club's representative at the convention.* 2 **Representative,** member of the House of Representatives. *n.*

re prieve (ri prēv′), 1 postpone the punishment of (a person), especially the execution of (a person condemned to death). 2 the order giving authority for such delay. 3 temporary relief from any evil or trouble. 1 *v.*, **re prieved, re priev ing;** 2,3 *n.*

re trieve (ri trēv′), 1 get again; recover. 2 bring back to a former or better condition; restore. 3 make good; make amends for; repair. 4 find and bring to a person. *v.*, **re trieved, re triev ing.**

rum mage sale (rum′ij), sale of odds and ends, old clothing, etc., usually held to raise money for charity.

ru mor (rü′mər), 1 story or statement talked of as news without any proof that it is true. 2 vague, general talk. 3 tell or spread by rumor. 1,2 *n.*, 3 *v.*

sand wich (sand′wich), two or more slices of bread with meat, jelly, cheese, or some other filling between them. *n., pl.* **sand wich es.** [from John Montagu, the fourth Earl of *Sandwich,* 1718-1792, who supposedly invented it]

schol ar ship (skol′ər ship), 1 possession of knowledge gained by study; quality of learning and knowledge. 2 money or other aid given to help a student continue his studies: *The college offered a scholarship of one thousand dollars. n.*

sen si tive (sen′sə tiv), 1 receiving impressions readily: *The eye is sensitive to light.* 2 easily affected or influenced: *The mercury in the thermometer is sensitive to changes in temperature.* 3 easily hurt or offended. *adj.* —**sen′si tive ly,** *adv.*

sen ti men tal (sen′tə men′tl), 1 having or showing much tender feeling: *sentimental poetry.* 2 likely to act from feelings rather than from logical thinking; having too much sentiment. *adj.*

se ra pe (sə rä′pē), shawl or blanket, often having bright colors, worn by Spanish Americans. *n.* Also, **sarape.**

serf (sėrf), 1 (in the feudal system) slave who could not be sold off the land, but passed from one owner to another with the land. 2 person treated almost like a slave; person who is mistreated, underpaid, etc. *n.*

ses a me (ses′ə mē), 1 the seeds of an Oriental plant, used to flavor bread, candy, and other foods, and in making an oil used in cooking. 2 plant producing these seeds. *n.* [from Greek *sēsamē;* of Semitic origin]

-ship, *suffix forming nouns from other nouns.* 1 office, position, or occupation of ____: *Governorship = office of governor. Authorship = occupation of an author.* 2 quality or condition of being____: *Partnership = condition of being a partner.* 3 act, power, or skill of ____: *Craftsmanship = skill of a craftsman.* 4 relation between____s: *Companionship = relation between companions.* [Old English -*scipe*]

shish ke bab (shish′ kə bob′), dish of cubed meat and vegetables roasted or broiled on skewers. [from Armenian *shish kabab*]

siege (sēj), 1 the surrounding of a fortified place by an army trying to capture it; a besieging or a being besieged: *Troy was under a siege for ten years.* 2 any long or persistent effort to overcome resistance; any long-continued attack: *a siege of illness. n.*

sir up (sir′əp *or* sėr′əp), syrup. *n.*

smog (smog), combination of smoke and fog in the air. *n.*

sou ve nir (sü′və nir′ *or* sü′və nir), something given or kept for remembrance; a remembrance; keepsake: *She bought a pair of moccasins as a souvenir of her trip out West. n.*

spec trum (spek′trəm), the band of colors formed when a beam of light is broken up by being passed through a prism or by some other means. A rainbow has all the colors of the spectrum: red, orange, yellow, green, blue, indigo, and violet. *n., pl.* **spec tra** (spek′trə), **spec trums.**

sul fur (sul′fər), a yellow, highly flammable, nonmetallic element that burns with a blue flame and a stifling odor. It is used in making matches, gunpowder, paper pulp, fertilizers, insecticides, etc. *n.* Also, **sulphur.**

su per in tend ent (sü′pər in ten′dənt), person who oversees, directs, or manages; supervisor: *a superintendent of schools, a superintendent of a factory or an apartment house. n.*

su per la tive (sə pér′lə tiv), **1** of the highest kind; above all others; supreme. **2** the highest degree of comparison of an adjective or adverb. *Fairest* and *most slowly* are the superlatives of *fair* and *slowly.* 1 *adj.,* 2 *n.*

sur pass (sər pas′), **1** do better than; be greater than; excel. **2** be too much or too great for; go beyond; exceed. *v.*

syn chro nize (sing′krə nīz), **1** occur at the same time; agree in time. **2** move or take place at the same rate and exactly together. **3** make agree in time: *synchronize all the clocks in a building. v.,* **syn chro nized, syn chro niz ing.**

syn thet ic (sin thet′ik), **1** made artificially by combining certain chemicals. Many kinds of fabrics, furs, dyes, rubbers, and drugs are synthetic products. **2** not real or genuine. **3 synthetics,** *pl.* man-made substances formed by combining certain chemicals. 1,2 *adj.,* 3 *n.*

syr up (sir′əp *or* sėr′əp), a sweet, thick liquid. Sugar boiled with water or fruit juices makes a syrup. Maple syrup is made from the sap of maple trees. *n.* Also, **sirup. —syr′up-like′,** *adj.*

ta co (tä′kō), tortilla filled with chopped meat, chicken, cheese, etc., and served hot. *n., pl.* **ta cos.** [from Mexican Spanish]

teak (tēk), **1** a large tree of the East Indies with a hard, durable, yellowish-brown wood. **2** this wood. Teak is used for shipbuilding. *n.*

tel e scope (tel′ ə skōp), **1** instrument for making distant objects appear nearer and larger. **2** force or be forced together one inside another like the sliding tubes of some telescopes. 1 *n.,* 2 *v.* **tel e scoped, tel e scop ing.**

telescope (definition 1)
The woman is using a telescope in an observatory. The object is enlarged either by a lens at the outer end of the telescope or by a large mirror at the inner end, which reflects into a smaller mirror placed opposite the eyepiece.

ter mi na tion (tėr′mə nā′shən), an ending; end: *Termination of the contract left both parties free to do business elsewhere. n.*

a hat	i it	oi oil	ch child	a in about
ā age	ī ice	ou out	ng long	e in taken
ä far	o hot	u cup	sh she	ə = i in pencil
e let	ō open	u̇ put	th thin	o in lemon
ē equal	ô order	ü rule	ŦH then	u in circus
ėr term			zh measure	

tex tile (tek′stəl *or* tek′stīl), **1** woven. **2** a woven fabric; cloth. **3** suitable for weaving: *Linen, cotton, silk, nylon, and wool are common textile materials.* **4** of or having to do with the making, selling, etc., of textiles. 1,3,4 *adj.,* 2 *n.*

tho or **tho'** (ŦHō), though. *conj., adv.*

though (ŦHō), **1** in spite of the fact that: *We take our medicine, though we do not like it.* **2** yet; still: *He is better, though not yet cured.* **3** even supposing that: *Though I fail, I shall try again.* **4** however: *I am sorry about our quarrel; you began it, though.* 1-3 *conj.,* 4 *adv.* Also, **tho** or **tho'.**

through (thrü), from end to end; from side to side; between the parts; from beginning to end. *adv.* Also, **thru.**

thru (thrü), through. *adv.*

tra di tion (trə dish′ən), **1** the handing down of beliefs, opinions, customs, stories, etc., from parents to children. **2** what is handed down in this way: *According to the old tradition, Romulus was the founder of Rome. n.*

traf fic (traf′ik), **1** people, automobiles, wagons, ships, etc., coming and going along a way of travel. **2** buying and selling; commerce; trade. **3** carry on trade; buy; sell; exchange. 1,2 *n.,* 3 *v.,* **traf ficked, traf fick ing.**

trait (trāt), quality of mind, character, etc.; characteristic: *Courage, love of fair play, and common sense are desirable traits. n.*

trans ac tion (tran zak′shən), **1** the carrying on (of business). **2** piece of business: *A record was kept of the firm's latest transaction with the bank.* **3 transactions,** *pl.* record of what was done at the meetings of a society, club, etc. *n.*

trans con ti nen tal (tran′skon tə nen′tl), **1** crossing a continent: *a transcontinental railroad.* **2** on the other side of a continent. *adj.*

trans fuse (tran sfyüz′), **1** pour from one container into another. **2** transfer (blood) from one person or animal to another. *v.,* **trans fused, trans fus ing.**

trans la tion (tran slā′shən), **1** a changing from one language into another. **2** result of translating; version. *n.*

trans par ent (tran sper′ənt *or* tran spar′ənt), **1** transmitting light so that bodies beyond or behind can be distinctly seen: *Window glass is transparent.* **2** easily seen through or detected: *a transparent excuse. adj.*

trans port (tran spôrt′ *for 1,5;* tran′spôrt *for 2-4*),
1 carry from one place to another. **2** a carrying
from one place to another. **3** ship used to carry
men and supplies. **4** aircraft that transports
passengers, mail, freight, etc. **5** carry away by
strong feeling: *He was transported with joy by the
good news.* 1,5 *v.,* 2-4 *n.*

treach er y (trech′ər ē), **1** a breaking of faith;
treacherous behavior; deceit. **2** treason. *n., pl.*
treach er ies.

trom bone (trom′bōn), a large brass wind
instrument with a loud tone, having a long,
sliding piece for varying the length of the tube. *n.*

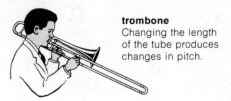

trombone
Changing the length
of the tube produces
changes in pitch.

tur moil (tèr′moil), state of agitation or commotion;
disturbance; tumult. *n.*

u ku le le (yü′kə lā′lē), a small guitar having four
strings. *n.* [from Hawaiian, originally, flea]

up stairs (up′sterz′ *or* up′starz′), **1** up the stairs.
2 on or to an upper floor: *She lives upstairs (adv.).
He is waiting in an upstairs hall (adj.).* 1,2 *adv.,* 2
adj.

-ure, *suffix added to verbs to form nouns.* **1** act or
fact of ___ ing: *Failure = act of failing.* **2** state of
being ___ ed: *Pleasure = state of being pleased.*
3 result of being ___ ed: *Exposure = result of
being exposed.* **4** something that ___ s: *Legislature
= something that legislates.* **5** thing that is ___ ed:
Disclosure = thing that is disclosed. [from French,
from Latin *-ura*]

vin e gar (vin′ə gər), a sour liquid produced by
the fermentation of cider, wine, malt, etc. Vinegar
is used in salad dressing and in flavoring or
preserving food. *n.*

vi rus (vī′rəs), any of a group of
disease-producing agents composed of protein
and nucleic acid. Viruses cause such diseases in
man as rabies, polio, chicken pox, and the
common cold. They are so small that they cannot
be seen through most microscopes. *n., pl.*
vi rus es.

vo ca tion (vō kā′shən), **1** occupation, business,
profession, or trade: *Teaching is her vocation.*
2 an inner call or summons. *n.*

ware (wer *or* war), **1** Usually, **wares,** *pl.* a
manufactured thing; article for sale.
2 earthenware; pottery: *porcelain ware. n.*

wrath (rath), very great anger; rage. *n.*

Picture Credits
p. 14, Robert Davis; p. 42, R/C Photo Agency, Richard L. Capps
(salad); p. 114, Robert Davis; p. 123, Robert Davis
(entertainment, excellent, people, captain's); Roxane McLean
(miniature and night); p. 139, Art Reference Bureau, Inc.
(Pantheon); Ewing Galloway (Parthenon)